# Curry Powder to Clinical Significance

Edited by:

Muhammed Majeed, Ph.D.

Anju Majeed, MS

Contributing Authors:

Bharat B. Aggarwal, Ph.D.

Kalyanam Nagabhushanam, Ph.D.

Anurag Pande, Ph.D.

Priti Vaidyanathan, Ph.D.

Mahadeva Nayak, M. Pharm

Sarang Bani, Ph.D.

Anjali Pandey, Ph.D.

First Printing

NutriScience Publishers, LLC

East Windsor, New Jersey

The information contained in this book, Curry Powder to Clinical Significance is intended for educational purposes only. It is not designed, in whole or in part, as advice for self-diagnosis or self-treatment; nor should this book or any statements made by its authors, be misconstrued as an endorsement of Curry Powder to Clinical Significance.

**NutriScience Publishers, LLC**
20 Lake Drive, East Windsor
New Jersey, 08520
The United States of America



NutriScience Publishers, LLC First Edition 2015
ISBN: 978-0-9883209-1-8

*Dedicated to*

# Dr. A. P. J. Abdul Kalam

Mentor • Scientist • The Missile Man

15 October 1931 - 27 July 2015

Dr. Abdul Kalam at Sami Labs Limited, Bangalore on 29th June, 2014

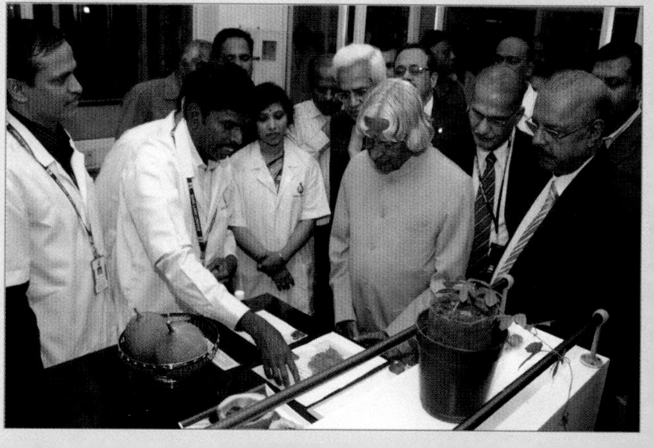

## Preface

*"The human body heals itself and nutrition provides the resources to accomplish the task."*
—Roger Williams

*When I set out on my journey from a small village in Kerala across oceans to the US, I went with my passion for science and with the determination that I will make a difference to the world of health and wellness. This led to the introduction of Ayurveda, an ancient Indian system of natural and holistic medicine to millions of Americans, making it one of the most popular complementary and integrated forms of medicine.*

*This successful integration of herbal remedies into mainstream medicine potentially contributed to its progression. Today, according to the World Health Organization (WHO), approximately 80% of people are dependent upon herbal medication for their primary healthcare necessities. There is thus a need that requires to be fulfilled, and the onus is on the scientific community to do the same.*

*Today, human lifestyles have changed drastically. Over the last few decades due to industrialization and changing work cultures people have been forced into various fast-eating cultures with more instant and tasty meals, but decreased the quality in nutrients. At the same time, industrialization has caused air and water pollution, contamination of soil and food because of extensive use of various chemicals, heavy metals, electromagnetic waves and other potentially harmful man-made materials. These problems have led to an increased incidence of several lifestyle-related disorders and it appears that natural plant-based remedies are the only solution to bail us out of this situation.*

*Among the numerous phytoextracts that we have introduced into the market for human nutrition, the most priceless plant extract would remain that of* ***Curcuma longa****. Curcuminoids, the versatile pronutrient, are undoubtedly one of the most important and precious gifts to mankind from Mother Nature. The research team from the Sami and Sabinsa group with the help of the research community globally, and working along with them and supporting them have clearly developed the medicinal and biochemical qualities that make this extract uniquely different.*

*My two earlier books on Curcuminoids were the first of its kind and addressed some of the fundamental aspects about the chemistry, pharmacology and applications of this wonder molecule. However, over the years, studies on Curcuminoids have grown exponentially and it is time yet again to share this knowledge to all who wish to benefit from it. The mechanism of Curcuminoids at the cellular level, laboratory experiments that indicate its potential applications and observations from hundreds of individuals suffering from various ailments who were benefitted by Curcumin have been compiled in this book.*

*Curcumin being one of such wonder phytonutrients—thanks to its powerful inherent properties, which work efficiently against several ailments and its long known traditional use has been evaluated and scientifically addressed in this book through numerous clinical studies that are relevant to modern health concerns.*

*In the current scenario, it has also become indispensable to transform experience-based claims about herbal use into evidence-based claims—to establish the credibility.*

*This concern has been addressed by the Sami-Sabinsa research team since 26 years successfully—to a great extent, and also substantiated the use of herbal medicine as a safe, effective and affordable form of healthcare—to strengthen more the concept of "integrated medicine".*

*I believe that this book was motivated by such desires to further the evolution of the interest in traditional therapies (alternative medicine) in the modern healthcare set-up.*

*Dr. Aggarwal's pioneering contribution in the understanding of his favourite golden spice is gratefully acknowledged.*

*I am greatly indebted to the innumerable number of scientists, who worked on the spice to understand the uniqueness of the product.*

*Wishing you and your loved ones the best of health today and always.*

*- Muhammed Majeed, Ph.D.*

# ABOUT THE EDITORS

## Muhammed Majeed, Ph.D.

*Dr. Muhammed Majeed holds a doctorate (1986) in Industrial Pharmacy from St. John's University, New York. He has over 15 years of pharmaceutical research experience in the United States with leading companies such as Pfizer Inc., Carter-Wallace and Paco Pharmaceuticals.*

*Subsequent to the formation of his company, Sabinsa Corporation in 1988, he has pursued his interest in phytochemistry and pharmaceutical sciences. He has led a team of scientists, both in India & USA, and obtained 102 US and International patents so far. He is aggressively pursuing his interest in natural products and continues to develop new products for the US and International markets.*

## Anju Majeed, MS

*Ms. Anju Majeed has been actively involved in various research and development activities at the Sami-Sabinsa group for over four years. She has a double masters degree in Microbiology and Molecular Genetics from Rutgers University and one from Johns Hopkins University, USA in Biological Sciences with focus on Genetics. She has also served as an NIH research scholar and is currently pursuing her Ph.D. in Microbiology at Bharathidasan University.*

## ABOUT THE AUTHORS

### Bharat B. Aggarwal, Ph.D.

*Dr. Bharat B. Aggarwal completed his doctorate in Biochemistry from the University of California, Berkeley and followed this with a post-doctoral fellowship in Endocrinology at the University of California, San Francisco. He has been with the MD Anderson Cancer Center in Houston, Texas since 1989 and is currently a professor pursuing research on cancer, biochemistry, immunology and experimental therapeutics. In addition, he is also the Director of the Cytokine Research Laboratory. Dr. Aggarwal has also served for 10 years as a molecular biologist and cancer researcher at Genentech Inc. contributing to several major scientific discoveries. He has over 500 scientific papers to his credit in journals including Science, Nature and Cancer. In 2008, he was awarded the McCormick Spice Research Institute Award from the American Society of Nutrition.*

### Kalyanam Nagabhushanam, Ph.D.

*Dr. Kalyanam Nagabhushanam is the President of Sami-Sabinsa group R&D. His research interests are in synthetic methodology, chiral chemistry and natural products. He obtained his M.Sc. in Chemistry from University of Madras and Ph.D. from Baylor, Texas. After a further two year post-doctoral studies in USA on chiral chemistry and chiro-optical methods, he returned to India to work for IPCL (now part of Reliance group), Ciba-Geigy (now known as Novartis) and SPIC Pharma. He has been with Sabinsa for the last 16 years. Dr. Kalyanam's primary reponsibilities at Sabinsa include the development of new products and exploration of new business areas.*

### Anurag Pande, Ph.D.

*Dr. Anurag Pande is the Vice-president - Scientific & Regulatory Affairs based in Sabinsa's New Jersey office. He has been with Sabinsa's parent company, Sami Labs, since 2004 in a research capacity and since 2008 has been based in Sabinsa Japan's Tokyo office as Senior Technical Manager. Dr. Pande holds a Ph.D. in Phytochemistry from RML Awadh University. He has both a Masters degree in Science and a Bachelor's degree in Science from Lucknow University.*

## Priti Vaidyanathan, Ph.D.

*Dr. Priti Vaidyanathan, with a Ph.D. specialization in Biochemistry from Bharathiar University, Coimbatore, has been closely involved with research activities related to Natural products and their biological activities for over a decade now. Currently heading the Technical Support Department at Sami Labs Ltd., she is into development and management of innovative research projects. Her current position in the company is an important bridge between the R&D team and the client/marketing team. A University gold medallist for her M.Sc., she has also won DST award and participated in several conferences/ workshops at the National and International arena. Her rich experience in natural product chemistry comes from post doctoral positions at Agricultural University and the Indian Institute of Science, Bangalore.*

## Mahadeva Nayak, M. Pharm

*Mr. Mahadeva Nayak has been with Sabinsa's parent company, Sami Labs Limited, since 2002 in R&D centre as a Scientist and since 2008 he holds the position of Manager - Technical Marketing, which primarily works as an interface between R&D and Business Development. He provides technical support to various Sami - Sabinsa representatives and clients for Business Development. He obtained his Masters degree in Pharmacy from Government College of Pharmacy, Bangalore and Bachelor degree in Pharmacy from College of Pharmaceutical Sciences, Manipal.*

## Sarang Bani, Ph.D.

*Dr. Sarang Bani is the Vice-president R&D - Biological Research, Sami Labs Limited. He has 33 years of research experience in the field of toxicology studies, cardiovascular, anti-inflammatory, anti-arthritic, obesity, anti-stress and neuro-degenerative studies. He is author of more than 150 publications in peer-reviewed international journals and 25 patents. He has been a guide for 5 students for Ph.D., 2 for M.D. and more than 30 students worked for their dissertation thesis in biotechnology, pharmacology, medicine, biochemistry etc. under his supervision. He is also an Editorial Board Member of reputed international journals.*

Anjali Pandey, Ph.D.

*Dr Anjali Pandey has 10 years of research experience in the field of biotechnology, molecular biology, anti-inflammatory, anti-arthritic, obesity, anti-stress and neuro-degenerative studies. She has done her Ph.D. from Council of Scientific & Industrial Research-Indian Institute of Integrative Medicine (CSIR-IIIM). She has authored 21 publications in peer-reviewed international journals, 12 patents and 16 abstracts. She is also a reviewer of many international scientific research journals.*

# PART ONE:
# Curcumin, My Golden Journey for Golden Spice from Golden City

*From Bedside to Bench and Back*



# PART TWO:
# Curcumin C3 Complex®

*The Most Clinically Studied Curcumin Brand in the World*

# *Curcumin,*
# *My Golden Journey for Golden Spice from Golden City*

From Bedside to Bench and Back

**Bharat B. Aggarwal, Ph.D.**
Cytokine Research Laboratory
Department of Experimental Therapeutics,
The University of Texas MD Anderson Cancer Center,
Houston, Texas, USA

# Abstract

More than 99% of the synthetic drugs made by man fail in the clinic either because they are too toxic to human subjects or they are ineffective. Drugs derived from natural products, however, are unique in that they have been used for thousands of years for a variety of diseases, but little is known either about the active component in them or the mechanism by which they manifest their effect. Turmeric is one such medicine that has been used as a spice for thousands of years and exhibits activities against a wide variety of diseases including viral, fungal and bacterial infections, inflammation, diabetes, cancer, skin diseases and others. There are now over 7,500 papers published on Curcumin. I personally come from the golden city (Amritsar, India) and my golden journey with the golden spice (Curcumin) started almost 25 years ago, when less than 50 papers were published on this subject. In this review, I describe the work carried out in my group with Curcumin, mainly **Curcumin C3 Complex**® consisting of Curcumin (75-81%), Demethoxycurcumin (15-19%) and Bisdemethoxycurcumin (2.2-6.5%).

Curcumin and Curcuminoids have been used interchangeably throughout this book, unless otherwise specified

# Introduction

The use of turmeric dates back nearly 4,000 years to the Vedic culture in India, where it was used as a culinary spice and had some religious significance. It probably reached China by 700 AD, East Africa by 800 AD, West Africa by 1200 AD and Jamaica in the $18^{th}$ century. In 1280 AD, Marco Polo-an Italian merchant traveler described this spice "marveling" at a vegetable that exhibited qualities so similar to that of saffron. According to Sanskrit medical treatises, Ayurvedic and Unani systems, turmeric has a long history of medicinal use in South Asia. Susruta's Ayurvedic Compendium, dating back to 250 BC recommends an ointment containing turmeric to relieve the effects of poisoned food. Today, turmeric is widely cultivated in the tropics and goes by different names in different cultures and countries.

Turmeric (*Curcuma longa*) is a spice that is golden yellow in color and is commonly used in the Indian subcontinent for healthcare, preservation of food as well as a yellow dye for textiles. Curcumin, which gives the yellow color to turmeric, was first isolated almost two centuries ago and its structure as diferuloylmethane was determined in 1910 [Aggarwal *et al.* 2007]. Since the time of Ayurveda (1900 BC) numerous therapeutic activities have been assigned to turmeric for a wide variety of diseases and conditions including those of the skin, pulmonary and gastrointestinal systems, aches, pains, wounds, sprains and liver disorders. Extensive research within the last half-a-century has proven that most of these activities, once associated with turmeric, are due to Curcumin. Curcumin has been shown to exhibit antioxidant, anti-inflammatory, antiviral, antibacterial, antifungal and anticancer activities. Thus, Curcumin has a potential against various malignant diseases, diabetes, allergies, arthritis, Alzheimer's disease and other chronic illnesses. These effects are mediated through the regulation of various transcription factors, growth factors, inflammatory cytokines, protein kinases and other enzymes. Curcumin exhibits activities similar to recently discovered tumor necrosis factor blockers (e.g. HUMIRA®, REMICADE® and ENBREL®), a vascular endothelial cell growth factor (VEGF) blocker (e.g. AVASTIN®), human epidermal growth factor receptor blockers (e.g. ERBITUX®, TARCEVA® and IRESSA®) and a human epidermal growth factor receptor (HER) 2 blocker (e.g. HERCEPTIN®). Considering the recent scientific bandwagon that multitargeted therapy is better than monotargeted therapy for most diseases, Curcumin can be considered an ideal "**Spice for Life**".

# Curcumin Chemistry

Curcumin has been shown to exhibit chemopreventive activity. Analogs of Curcumin such as Demethoxycurcumin (DMC), Bisdemethoxycurcumin (BDMC), Tetrahydrocurcumin (THC) and turmerones were investigated as to whether they modulate inflammatory signaling and cell proliferation signaling to same extent as Curcumin [Sandur *et al.* 2007a]. Tetrahydrocurcumin for this study was supplied by Sabinsa.

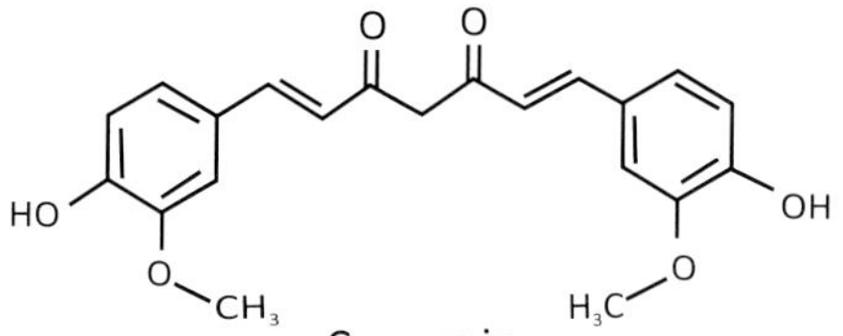


Curcumin

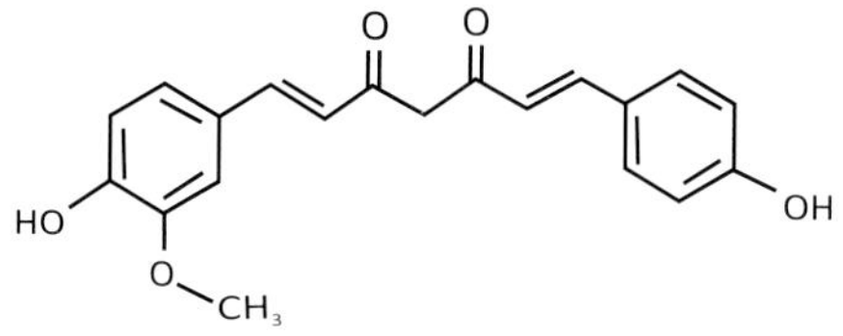


Demethoxycurcumin

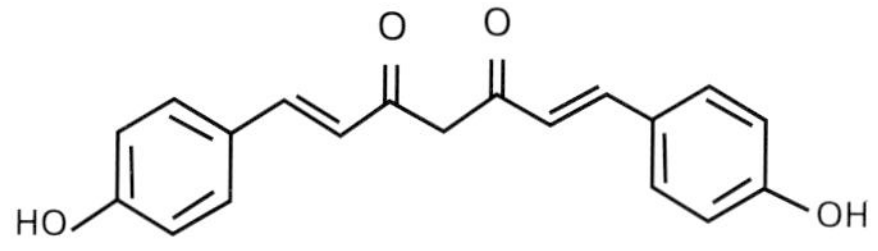


Bisdemethoxycurcumin

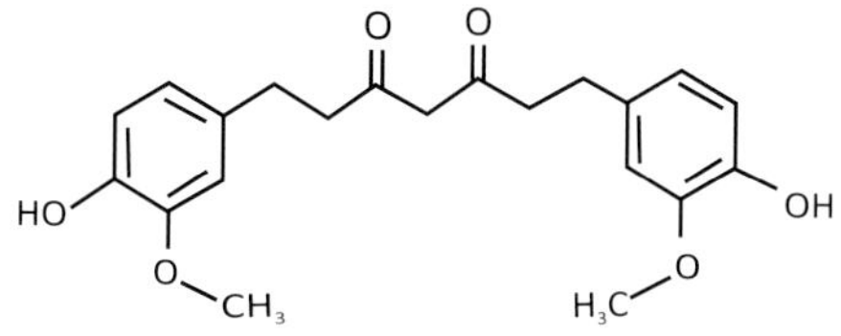


Tetrahydrocurcumin

The results indicated that the relative potency for suppression of TNF-α-induced nuclear factor-κB (NF-κB) activation was Curcumin > Demethoxycurcumin > Bisdemethoxycurcumin, thus suggesting the critical role of methoxy groups on the phenyl ring. Tetrahydrocurcumin, which lacks the conjugated bonds in the central seven-carbon chain was completely inactive for suppression of the transcription factor. Turmerones also failed to inhibit TNF-α-induced NF-κB activation. The suppression of NF-κB activity correlated with inhibition of NF-κB reporter activity and with downregulation of cyclooxygenase-2 (COX-2), cyclin D1 and vascular endothelial growth factor (VEGF), all regulated by NF-κB. In contrast to NF-κB activity, the suppression of proliferation of various tumor cell lines by Curcumin, Demethoxycurcumin and Bisdemethoxycurcumin was found to be comparable; indicating the methoxy groups play minimum role in the growth-modulatory effects of Curcumin. Tetrahydrocurcumin and turmerones were also found to be active in suppression of cell growth but to a much lesser extent than Curcumin, Demethoxycurcumin and Bisdemethoxycurcumin. No relationship of any of the curcuminoid was found with reactive oxygen species (ROS) production whether suppression of NF-κB or cell proliferation. Overall, our results demonstrated that different analogs of Curcumin that are present in turmeric exhibit variable anti-inflammatory and anti-proliferative activities, which do not correlate with their ability to modulate the reactive oxygen species status.

Curcumin has been shown to exhibit anti-inflammatory and anti-proliferative activities. While Curcumin has both Michael acceptor and a Michael donor units, its analogues Dibenzoylmethane (a component of licorice) and Dibenzoylpropane have a Michael donor but not a Michael acceptor unit and the analogue Dibenzylideneacetone has a Michael acceptor unit. We investigated the potency of Dibenzoylmethane, Dibenzoylpropane and Dibenzylideneacetone in relation to Curcumin (purity higher than 95% supplied by Sabinsa Corporation) for their ability to suppress TNF-α-induced NF-κB activation, NF-κB-regulated gene products and cell proliferation [Anand *et al.* 2011]. We found that all four agents were active in suppressing NF-κB activation. Curcumin was the most active and Dibenzoylmethane was the least. When examined for its ability to inhibit the direct DNA binding activity of p65, a subunit of NF-κB, only Dibenzoylpropane inhibited the binding and Dibenzylideneacetone was most active in inhibiting TNF-α-induced IκB-alpha kinase (IKK) activation. Dibenzylideneacetone and Curcumin were more active than Dibenzoylmethane in suppressing TNF-α-induced expression of NF-κB-regulated gene products such as COX-2 (inflammation marker), cyclin D1 (proliferation marker) and vascular endothelial growth factor (angiogenesis marker). Similarly, Curcumin and Dibenzylideneacetone were most active and Dibenzoylpropane was the least active in suppression of proliferation of leukemia, T cell leukemia, prostate and breast cancer cells. Overall, our results indicated that although Curcumin and its analogues exhibit activities to suppress inflammatory pathways and cellular proliferation, a lack of Michael acceptor units in Dibenzoylmethane and Dibenzoylpropane can reduce their activities.

The utility of Curcumin is limited by its color, lack of water solubility and relatively low *in vivo* bioavailability [Anand *et al.* 2008]. Hence, there is an intense search for a "Super Curcumin" addressing the above mentioned limitations since Curcumin is attributed to several therapeutic activities. Multiple approaches are being sought to overcome these limitations. These include discovery of natural Curcumin analogues from turmeric made by Mother Nature; synthesis of "man-made" Curcumin analogues; reformulation of Curcumin with various oils and with inhibitors of metabolism (e.g., Piperine); development of liposomal and nanoparticle formulations of Curcumin; conjugation of Curcumin prodrugs and linking Curcumin with polyethylene glycol. Curcumin is a homodimer of feruloylmethane containing a methoxy group and a hydroxyl group, a heptadiene with two Michael acceptors and an alpha, beta-diketone. Structural homologues involving modification of all these groups are being considered. This review focuses on the status of all these approaches in generating a "Super Curcumin".

As mentioned earlier, Curcumin has been linked with antioxidant, anti-inflammatory, anticancer, antiviral, antibacterial and antidiabetic properties. Most of these activities have been assigned to methoxy, hydroxyl, $\alpha$, $\beta$-unsaturated carbonyl moiety or to diketone groups present in Curcumin [Aggarwal *et al.* 2014]. One of the major metabolites of Curcumin is Tetrahydrocurcumin, which lacks $\alpha$, $\beta$-unsaturated carbonyl moiety and is white in color. The superiority of Tetrahydrocurcumin to Curcumin at molecular levels is unclear. Various studies suggested that Curcumin is a more potent antioxidant than Tetrahydrocurcumin; Curcumin (but not Tetrahydrocurcumin) can bind and inhibit numerous targets including DNA (cytosine-5)-methyltransferase-1, heme oxygenase-1, Nrf2, $\beta$-catenin, COX-2, NF-$\kappa$B, inducible nitric oxide synthase (iNOS), nitric oxide, amyloid plaques, reactive oxygen species, vascular endothelial growth factor, cyclin D1, glutathione, P300/CBP, 5-lipoxygenase, cytosolic phospholipase A2, prostaglandin E2, inhibitor of NF-$\kappa$B kinase-1, 2, P38MAPK, p-Tau, TNF-$\alpha$, forkhead box O3a and $Ca^{+2}$-release activated $Ca^{+2}$ channel (CRAC). Curcumin can inhibit tumor cell growth and suppress cellular entry of viruses such as influenza A and hepatitis C much more effectively than Tetrahydrocurcumin. Curcumin affects membrane mobility and is also more effective than Tetrahydrocurcumin in suppressing phorbol-ester-induced tumor promotion. Other studies, however, suggested that Tetrahydrocurcumin is superior to Curcumin for induction of glutathione peroxidase, glutathione-S-transferase, NADPH: quinone reductase and quenching of free radicals. Most studies have indicated that Tetrahydrocurcumin exhibits higher antioxidant activity but Curcumin exhibits both pro-oxidant and antioxidant properties.

Novel Curcumin analogs were synthesized using Knoevenagel condensation to convert enolic diketones of Curcumin into non-enolizable ones and Schiff bases were prepared using a bioactive thiosemicarbazide pharmacophore [Zambre *et al.* 2006]. Copper(II) conjugates of all synthesized ligands were prepared and structurally characterized as well as evaluated for their potential of inhibiting TNF-α-induced NF-κB activation and proliferation in human leukemic KBM-5 cells, wherein a specific analogue was found to be more potent than Curcumin. Compounds were further examined on other tumor cell lines such as Jurkat, H1299 and MM1.

A gram scale synthesis of glucuronide metabolites of Curcumin was completed in four steps. The newly synthesized Curcumin glucuronide compounds namely mono-glucuronide and di-glucuronide along with Curcumin were tested for their anti-proliferative effects against KBM-5, Jurkat cell, U266 and A549 cell lines [Pal *et al.* 2014]. Biological data revealed that as much as 1 μM Curcumin exhibited anticancer activity and almost 100% cell death was noted at 10 μM on two out of four cell lines; while Curcumin mono-glucuronide as well as di-glucuronide displayed no suppression of cell proliferation.

In a search of new compounds active against cancer, synthesis of a series of C-5 Curcumin analogues was carried out [Anthwal *et al.* 2014]. The new compounds demonstrated good cytotoxicity against chronic myeloid leukemia and colon cancer cell lines. Further, these compounds were found to have better potential to inhibit TNF-α-induced NF-κB activation in comparison to Curcumin, which show their potential to act as anti-inflammatory agents. Some compounds were found to show higher cytotoxicity against cancer cell lines in comparison to Curcumin used as standard.

# *Curcumin as Anti-inflammatory Agent* (NF-κB, TNF-α, STAT3)

## Curcumin as Inhibitor of NF-κB

When activated, NF-κB, a ubiquitous transcription factor, binds to DNA as a heterodimeric complex composed of members of the Rel/NF-κB family of polypeptides. It is an important target for therapeutic intervention due to its intimate involvement in host defense against disease. We demonstrated that Curcumin, a known anti-inflammatory and anticarcinogenic agent, is a potent inhibitor of NF-κB activation [Singh and Aggarwal. 1995]. Treatment of human myeloid ML-1α cells with tumor necrosis factor rapidly activated NF-κB, which consists of p50 and p65 subunits, and this activation was inhibited by Curcumin. Activator protein 1(AP-1) binding factors were also found to be down-modulated by Curcumin, whereas the Sp1 binding factor was unaffected. Besides TNF-α, Curcumin also blocked phorbol ester and hydrogen peroxide-mediated activation of NF-κB. Tumor necrosis factor-α-dependent phosphorylation and degradation of IκB-alpha were not observed in Curcumin-treated cells but inhibition of the translocation of p65 subunit to the nucleus was seen. The mechanism of action of Curcumin was found to be different from that of protein tyrosine phosphatase inhibitors. Our results indicated that Curcumin inhibits NF-κB activation pathway at a step before IκB-alpha phosphorylation but after the convergence of various stimuli.

## Curcumin as Inhibitor of COX-2

Non-steroidal anti-inflammatory drugs (NSAIDs) such as Aspirin have been shown to suppress transcription factor NF-κB, which controls the expression of genes such as COX-2 and cyclin D1, leading to inhibition of proliferation of tumor cells. There is no systematic study as to how these drugs differ in their ability to suppress NF-κB activation and NF-κB-regulated gene expression or cell proliferation. We investigated the effect of almost a dozen different commonly used non-steroidal anti-inflammatory drugs on TNF-α-induced NF-κB activation and NF-κB-regulated gene products and on cell proliferation [Takada *et al.* 2004]. Dexamethasone, an anti-inflammatory steroid, was included for comparison with non-steroidal anti-inflammatory drugs. As indicated by DNA binding, none of the drugs alone activated NF-κB. All compounds inhibited TNF-α-induced NF-κB activation but with highly variable efficacy.

**Table:** The table represents the $IC_{50}$ (50% inhibitory concentration) values of different test samples in inhibiting TNF-α-induced NF- κB activation and proliferation of tumor cells.

| Test Samples | $IC_{50}$ concentration required to inhibit TNF-α-induced NF-κB activation (mM) | $IC_{50}$ concentration required to inhibit the proliferation of tumor cells (mM) |
|---|---|---|
| Aspirin | 5.67 | 6.09 |
| Ibuprofen | 3.49 | 1.12 |
| Sulindac | 3.03 | 0.65 |
| Phenylbutazone | 1.25 | 0.49 |
| Naproxen | 0.94 | 1.01 |
| Indomethacin | 0.60 | 0.19 |
| Diclofenac | 0.38 | 0.36 |
| Resveratrol | 0.084 | 0.012 |
| Curcumin | 0.043 | 0.016 |
| Dexamethasone | 0.027 | 0.047 |
| Celecoxib | 0.024 | 0.013 |
| Tamoxifen | 0.010 | 0.008 |

All drugs inhibited IκB-alpha kinase and suppressed IκB-alpha degradation and NF-κB-regulated reporter gene expression. They also suppressed NF-κB-regulated COX-2 and cyclin D1 protein expression in a dose-dependent manner. All compounds inhibited the proliferation of tumor cells. Overall, these results indicated that aspirin and ibuprofen are least potent, while resveratrol, Curcumin, celecoxib and tamoxifen are the most potent anti-inflammatory and anti-proliferative agents of those we studied.

## Curcumin as Inhibitor of STAT3

Numerous reports suggested that interleukin-6 promotes survival and proliferation of multiple myeloma cells through the phosphorylation of a cell signaling protein, signal transducer and activator of transcription-3 (STAT3). Thus, agents that suppress STAT3 phosphorylation have potential for the treatment of multiple myeloma. We demonstrated that Curcumin inhibited interleukin-6-induced STAT3 phosphorylation and consequent nuclear translocation [Bharti *et al.* 2003a]. Curcumin had no effect on signal transducer and activator of transcription-5 phosphorylation but inhibited the interferon-α-induced signal transducer and activator of transcription-1 phosphorylation. The constitutive phosphorylation of STAT3 found in certain multiple myeloma cells was also abrogated by treatment with Curcumin. Curcumin-induced inhibition of STAT3 phosphorylation was reversible. Compared with AG490, a well-characterized Janus kinase 2 inhibitor, Curcumin was a more rapid (30 min vs 8 h) and more potent (10 μM vs 100 μM) inhibitor of STAT3 phosphorylation. In a similar manner, 10μM of Curcumin completely suppressed proliferation of multiple myeloma cells while same dose of AG490 had no effect. In contrast, a cell-permeable STAT3 inhibitor peptide that can inhibit the STAT3 phosphorylation mediated by Src blocked the constitutive phosphorylation of STAT3 and also suppressed the growth of myeloma cells. Tumor necrosis factor-α and lymphotoxin also induced the proliferation of multiple myeloma cells but through a mechanism independent of STAT3 phosphorylation. In addition, dexamethasone-resistant multiple myeloma cells were found to be sensitive to Curcumin. Overall, our results demonstrated that Curcumin was a potent inhibitor of STAT3 phosphorylation, which plays a role in the suppression of multiple myeloma proliferation.

 

## Curcumin as Inhibitor of TNF-α

Tumor necrosis factor-α is a cell signaling cytokine that is associated with systemic inflammatory processes in the body. The United States Food and Drug Administration (USFDA) has approved the use of blockers of the TNF-α for the treatment of osteoarthritis, inflammatory bowel disease, psoriasis and ankylosis. These drugs include the chimeric TNF-α antibody (Infliximab), humanized TNF-α antibody (HUMIRA®) and soluble TNF-α receptor-II (ENBREL®) and are associated with a total cumulative market value of more than $20 billion a year. As well as being expensive ($15,000-20,000 per person per year), these drugs have to be injected and have enough adverse effects to be given a black label warning by the USFDA. In the current report, we described Curcumin as an alternative that can block TNF-α production, its effect in *in vitro* models, animal models and in humans [Aggarwal *et al.* 2013]. In addition, we have provided evidence for Curcumin's activities against all inflammatory diseases for which TNF-α blockers are currently being used. Mechanisms by which Curcumin inhibits the production of TNF-α and blocks the cell signaling pathways activated by this cytokine are also discussed. With healthcare costs and safety being major issues today, this golden spice may help provide the solution.

# *Modulation of Immune System by Curcumin*

## Curcumin as Inhibitor of Adhesion Molecules

Recruitment of leukocytes by endothelial cells and their subsequent migration from the vasculature into the tissue plays a major role in inflammation. In the present study, we investigated the effect of Curcumin on the adhesion of monocytes to human umbilical vein endothelial cells [Kumar *et al.* 1998]. Treatment of endothelial cells with TNF-α for 6 h augmented the adhesion of monocytes to endothelial cells, which was due to increased expression of intracellular adhesion molecule-1 (ICAM-1), vascular cell adhesion molecule-1 (VCAM-1) and endothelial leukocyte adhesion molecule-1 (ELAM-1). Pretreatment of endothelial cells for 1 h with Curcumin completely blocked their adhesion to monocytes, as well as the cell surface expression of all three adhesion molecules. Although Curcumin inhibited adhesion even when administered 1 h after TNF-α treatment, maximum inhibition occurred when added either 1 h before or at the same time as TNF-α. As the induction of various adhesion molecules by TNF-α requires activation of the transcription factor NF-κB, the effect of Curcumin on the activation of this factor in the endothelial cells was also investigated. Pretreatment with Curcumin resulted in inhibition of TNF-α activated NF-κB activation (30 min treatment) in a concentration-dependent manner. This shows that NF-κB inhibition may play a role in the suppression of expression of adhesion molecules in endothelial cells. Our results demonstrated that anti-inflammatory properties of Curcumin may be attributable, in part, to inhibition of leukocyte recruitment.

## Curcumin as Inhibitor of Cytokine Expression

In the last two decades Curcumin has been shown to be a potent immunomodulatory agent that can modulate the activation of T cells, B cells, macrophages, neutrophils, natural killer cells and dendritic cells. Curcumin can also downregulate the expression of various pro-inflammatory cytokines including TNF-α, interleukin-1, interleukin-6, interleukin-8, interleukin-12 and chemokines most likely through inactivation of the transcription factor NF-κB [Jagetia and Aggarwal. 2007]. Interestingly, Curcumin at low doses can also enhance antibody responses by activating B cells. This suggests that Curcumin's reported beneficial effects in arthritis, allergy, asthma, atherosclerosis, heart disease, Alzheimer's disease, diabetes and cancer might be due in part to its ability to modulate the immune system. Together, these findings warrant further consideration of Curcumin as a therapy for immune disorders.

# *Curcumin as Antioxidant*

We investigated whether the anti-inflammatory and pro-apoptotic activities assigned to Curcumin are mediated through its pro-oxidant/antioxidant mechanism. We found that TNF-α-mediated NF-κB activation was inhibited by Curcumin and glutathione reversed the inhibition. Similarly, suppression of TNF-α-induced protein kinase B (PKB, also known as Akt) activation by Curcumin was also abrogated by glutathione. The reducing agent also counteracted the inhibitory effects of Curcumin on TNF-α-induced NF-κB-regulated antiapoptotic (Bcl-2), proliferative (cyclin D1) and pro-inflammatory such as COX-2 and inducible nitric oxide synthase gene products. The suppression of TNF-α-induced AP-1 activation by Curcumin was also reversed by glutathione [Sandur *et al.* 2007b]. Also, the direct pro-apoptotic effects of Curcumin were inhibited by glutathione and potentiated by depletion of intracellular glutathione by buthionine sulfoximine. Moreover, Curcumin induced the production of reactive oxygen species and modulated intracellular glutathione levels. Quenchers of hydroxyl radicals, however, were ineffective in inhibiting Curcumin-mediated NF-κB suppression. Further, N-acetylcysteine partially reversed the effect of Curcumin. Based on these results, we concluded that Curcumin mediates its apoptotic and anti-inflammatory activities through modulation of the oxidation-reduction (REDOX) status of the cell.

# Curcumin as Chemosensitizer

Extensive research within the last decade in cell culture and in rodents has revealed that Curcumin can sensitize tumors to different chemotherapeutic agents including doxorubicin, 5-fluorouracil, paclitaxel, vincristine, melphalan, cisplatin, celecoxib, vinorelbine, oxaliplatin, sulfinosine, thalidomide and bortezomib [Goel and Aggarwal. 2010]. Chemosensitization has been observed in cancers of the breast, colon, pancreas, gastric, liver, blood, lung, prostate, bladder, cervix, ovary, head and neck, brain, in multiple myeloma, leukemia and lymphoma. Similar studies have also revealed that this agent can sensitize a variety of tumors to gamma radiation including glioma, neuroblastoma, cervical carcinoma, epidermal carcinoma, prostate cancer and colon cancer. It has also been extensively studied to understand how Curcumin acts as a chemosensitizer. For example, it downregulates various growth regulatory pathways including genes for NF-κB, STAT3, COX-2, Akt, antiapoptotic proteins, growth factor receptors and multidrug-resistance proteins. Although it acts as a chemosensitizer for tumors in some cases, Curcumin has also been shown to protect normal organs such as liver, kidney, oral mucosa and heart from chemotherapy and radiotherapy-induced toxicity. The protective effects of Curcumin appear to be mediated through its ability to induce the expression of antioxidant enzymes (e.g. hemeoxygenase-1, glutathione peroxidase and NADPH:quinone oxidoreductase 1, increase glutathione), directly quench free radicals and inhibit p300 histone acetyltransferase (HAT) activity. These preclinical studies are expected to lead to clinical trials to prove the potential of this age-old golden spice for treating cancer patients.

# Curcumin as Radiosensitizer

Radiation therapy is an integral part of the preoperative treatment of rectal cancers. However, only a minority of patients achieve a complete pathologic response to therapy because of resistance of these tumors to radiation therapy. This resistance may be mediated by constitutively active pro-survival signaling pathways or by inducible mechanisms in response to radiation therapy. Simultaneous inhibition of these pathways can sensitize these tumors to radiation therapy. Human colorectal cancer cells were exposed to clinically relevant doses of gamma rays and the mechanism of their radioresistance was investigated [Sandur *et al.* 2009]. We characterized the transcription factor NF-κB activation as a mechanism of inducible radioresistance in colorectal cancer and used Curcumin to overcome this resistance. Curcumin inhibited the proliferation and the post-irradiation clonogenic survival of multiple colorectal cancer cell lines. Radiation-stimulated NF-κB activity in a dose and time-dependent manner, whereas Curcumin suppressed this radiation-induced NF-κB activation via inhibition of radiation-induced phosphorylation and degradation of inhibitor of IκB-apha, inhibition of inhibitor of IκB kinase activity and inhibition of Akt phosphorylation. Curcumin also suppressed NF-κB-regulated gene products (Bcl-2, Bcl-xL, inhibitor of apoptosis protein-2, COX-2 and cyclin D1). Our results suggested that transient inducible NF-κB activation provide a prosurvival response to radiation that may account for development of radioresistance. Curcumin blocks this signaling pathway and potentiates the antitumor effects of radiation therapy.

The transcription factor NF-κB and NF-κB-regulated gene products have been proposed as mediators causing resistance to gamma-radiation. Since Curcumin has been shown to suppress NF-κB activation, whether it can sensitize the colorectal cancer to gamma-radiation was investigated in colorectal cancer xenografts in nude mice [Kunnumakkara *et al.* 2008]. We established HCT 116 xenograft in nude mice, randomized into four groups and treated with vehicle (corn oil), Curcumin C3 Complex®, gamma-radiation and Curcumin C3 Complex® in combination with gamma-radiation. NF-κB modulation was ascertained using electrophoretic mobility shift assay and immunohistochemistry. Markers of proliferation, angiogenesis and invasion were monitored by immunohistochemistry and Western blot analysis. Curcumin C3 Complex® significantly enhanced the efficacy of fractionated radiation therapy by prolonging the time to tumor regrowth and by reducing the Ki-67 proliferation index. Moreover, Curcumin suppressed NF-κB activity and the expression of NF-κB-regulated gene products, many of which were induced by radiation therapy and mediate radioresistance. The combination of Curcumin and radiation therapy also suppressed angiogenesis, as indicated by a decrease in vascular endothelial growth factor and microvessel density. Collectively, our results suggested that Curcumin C3 Complex® potentiates the antitumor effects of radiation therapy in colorectal cancer by suppressing NF-κB and NF-κB-regulated gene products leading to inhibition of proliferation and angiogenesis.

# Curcumin as Anticancer Agent

Extensive research over the last 20 years has indicated that Curcumin can both prevent and treat cancer [Aggarwal *et al.* 2003]. The anticancer potential of Curcumin stems from its ability to suppress proliferation of a wide variety of tumor cells, downregulate transcription factors NF-κB, AP-1 and Egr-1, downregulate the expression of pro-inflammatory cytokines, chemokines and mediators, downregulate growth factor receptors (such as epidermal growth factor receptor (EGFR) and human epidermal growth factor receptor 2) and inhibit the activity of c-Jun N-terminal kinase, protein tyrosine kinases and protein serine/threonine kinases. In several systems, Curcumin has been described as a potent antioxidant and anti-inflammatory agent. Evidence has also been presented to suggest that Curcumin can suppress tumor initiation, promotion and metastasis. Pharmacologically, Curcumin has been found to be safe. Human clinical trials indicated no dose-limiting toxicity when administered at doses up to 10 g/day. All of these studies suggest that Curcumin has enormous potential in the prevention and therapy of cancer. The current review describes in detail the data supporting these studies.

## Role of Curcumin in Leukemia

Pharmacologically safe compounds that can inhibit the proliferation of tumor cells have potential as anticancer agents. Curcumin has been shown to inhibit the proliferation of a wide variety of leukemia cells [Anto *et al.* 2002]. The apoptotic intermediates through which Curcumin exhibits its cytotoxic effects against tumor cells are not known and the participation of antiapoptotic proteins Bcl-2 or Bcl-xL in the Curcumin-induced apoptosis pathway is not established. The effect of Curcumin on the activation of the apoptotic pathway was investigated in human acute myelogenous leukemia HL-60 cells and in established stable cell lines expressing Bcl-2 and Bcl-xL. Curcumin inhibited the growth of HL-60 cells (neo) in a dose and time-dependent manner, whereas Bcl-2 and Bcl-xL-transfected cells were relatively resistant. Curcumin activated caspase-8 and caspase-3 in HL-60 neo cells but not in Bcl-2 and Bcl-xL-transfected cells. Similarly, time-dependent poly(ADP)ribose polymerase (PARP) cleavage by Curcumin was observed in neo cells but not in Bcl-2 and Bcl-xL-transfected cells. Curcumin treatment also induced BID cleavage and mitochondrial cytochrome c release in neo cells but not in Bcl-2 and Bcl-xL-transfected cells. In neo HL-60 cells, Curcumin also downregulated the expression of COX-2. Data also revealed that caspase-8 may play a critical role since DN-FLICE blocked curcumin induced apoptosis. Overall, our results indicated that Curcumin induces apoptosis through mitochondrial pathway involving caspase-8, BID cleavage, cytochrome c release and caspase-3 activation. Our results also suggested that Bcl-2 and Bcl-xL are critical negative regulators of Curcumin-induced apoptosis.

## Role of Curcumin in Multiple Myeloma

The central role of the transcription factor NF-κB in cell survival and proliferation in human multiple myeloma has been reported [Bharti *et al.* 2003b]. We evaluated the possibility of using NF-κB as a molecular target for Curcumin in an attempt to elucidate the therapeutic potential of Curcumin for multiple myeloma. We found that NF-κB was constitutively active in all human multiple myeloma cell lines examined. Curcumin, a known chemopreventive agent, downregulated NF-κB in all cell lines as indicated by electrophoretic mobility gel shift assay. Curcumin was also shown to prevent the nuclear retention of p65 as shown by immunocytochemistry. All multiple myeloma cell lines showed consitutively active IκB kinase and IκB-alpha phosphorylation. Curcumin suppressed the constitutive IκB-alpha phosphorylation through the inhibition of IκB kinase activity. Curcumin also downregulated the expression of NF-κB-regulated gene products including IκB-alpha, Bcl-2, Bcl-xL, cyclin D1 and interleukin-6. This led to the suppression of proliferation and arrest of cells at the G(1)/S phase of the cell cycle. Suppression of NF-κB complex by IKK gamma/NF-κB essential modulator-binding domain peptide also suppressed the proliferation of multiple myeloma cells. Curcumin also activated caspase-7 and caspase-9 and induced polyadenosine-5'-diphosphate-ribose polymerase cleavage. Curcumin-induced downregulation of NF-κB, a factor that has been implicated in chemoresistance, also induced chemosensitivity to vincristine and melphalan. Overall, our results indicated that Curcumin downregulates NF-κB in human multiple myeloma cells, leading to the suppression of proliferation and induction of apoptosis. It was thus shown that Curcumin evidenced the therapeutic potential towards the management of multiple myeloma with effects at the cellular and molecular levels.

Chemoresistance is a major problem in the treatment of patients with multiple myeloma. Since nuclear transcription factors NF-κB and STAT3 play a central role in chemoresistance, cell survival and proliferation, we investigated whether multiple myeloma cells derived from patients express activated NF-κB and STAT3 and if their suppression induces apoptosis [Bharti *et al.* 2004a]. CD138+ cells from the bone marrow of multiple myeloma patients were assayed and checked for the activated forms of NF-κB and STAT3 by immunocytochemistry. We found that multiple myeloma cells from all the patients expressed the activated forms of NF-κB and STAT3 but to a variable degree. Constitutive activation of NF-κB in some cases was also independently confirmed by electrophoretic mobility gel shift assay. In contrast to multiple myeloma patients, activated forms of NF-κB and STAT3 were absent in cells from healthy individuals. Suppression of NF-κB and STAT3 activation in multiple myeloma cells by *ex vivo* treatment with Curcumin (diferuloylmethane) resulted in a decrease in adhesion to bone marrow stromal cells, cytokine secretion and in the viability of cells. When compared with Curcumin, dexamethasone was less effective in suppression of NF-κB activation and induction of apoptosis in myeloma cells. Overall, our results indicated that fresh cells from multiple myeloma patients express constitutively active NF-κB and STAT3 and suppression of these transcription factors inhibits the survival of the cells.

## Clinical Study

The role of NF-κB and STAT3 in proliferation and metastasis of various tumor cells is well established. However, no agent has yet been described which could downregulate the activation of these transcription factors in cancer patients. Curcumin has been shown to potently suppress the activation of this transcription factor in cultured cells, however, it is not known whether it can downregulate NF-κB and STAT3 in cancer patients. Based on these observations, a clinical trial of Curcumin C3 Complex® alone (administered orally at 2, 4, 6, 8, or 12 g/day in 2 divided doses) or in combination with BioPerine® (10 mg in 2 divided doses) was carried out for 12 weeks in multiple myeloma patients [Vadhan-Raj *et al.* 2007]. The objectives of this study were to evaluate the safety, clinical tolerance and biological effects of Curcumin in multiple myeloma patients who had asymptomatic, relapsed or plateau phase disease. Blood was collected before and after treatment with Curcumin for limited PK/PD. Peripheral blood mononuclear cells (PBMCs) were examined (baseline and during treatment) to evaluate the effect of treatment on expression of NF-κB, p65, COX-2 and pSTAT3 as surrogate biomarkers. NF-κB activation status was also measured by electrophoretic mobility shift assay (EMSA). At least six patients were enrolled at each dose level; three on Curcumin alone arm and three on Curcumin + BioPerine® arm. The patients with at least a stable disease symptom were allowed to continue treatment upto one year. Treatment with Curcumin and a fixed dose of BioPerine® has been well tolerated with no significant adverse events. At 12 g dose level, two of the five patients had difficulty in swallowing the large number of capsules. Of the 29 evaluable patients treated so far, 12 patients showing stable disease conditions continued treatment for more than 12 weeks and five (one patient at 4 g, two at 6 g and two at 8 g dose levels) have completed full one year of treatment. Total Curcumin levels (mostly conjugated drug) in plasma were dose-dependent and was also dependent on the duration of administration. Peripheral blood mononuclear cells from 28 cancer patients examined at baseline showed constitutively active expression of NF-κB, COX-2 and STAT3. Oral administration of Curcumin significantly downregulated the constitutive activation of NF-κB, STAT3 and suppressed COX-2 expression in most of the patients at each of the monthly time points for 3 months. To conclude, the study was first to report that Curcumin is a highly safe agent, bioavailable and can downregulate NF-κB, STAT3 and COX-2 expressions in multiple myeloma patients. The study also suggested a potential therapeutic role that can be further investigated.

## Role of Curcumin in Head and Neck Squamous Cell Carcinoma

Head and neck squamous cell carcinoma (HNSCC) is a type of cancer in which increased expression of pro-inflammatory and proangiogenic factors are associated with aggressive tumor growth and decreased survival of patients. Genes that are regulated by NF-κB suppress apoptosis, induce proliferation and mediate inflammation, angiogenesis and tumor metastasis. Agents that suppress NF-κB activation have potential as treatment for various cancers including head and neck squamous cell carcinoma [Aggarwal *et al.* 2004]. We demonstrated that all head and neck squamous cell carcinoma cell lines expressed constitutively active NF-κB and IκB-alpha kinase, which is required for NF-κB activation. Treatment of MDA 686LN cells with Curcumin inhibited NF-κB activation through abrogation of IκB-alpha kinase. As a result, expression of various cell survival and cell proliferative genes including Bcl-2, cyclin D1, interleukin-6, COX-2 and matrix metallopeptidase-9 (MMP-9) were suppressed. This, in turn, inhibited proliferation of all head and neck squamous cell carcinoma cell lines by arresting the cell cycle in G1/S phase (MDA 686LN) and inducing apoptosis as indicated by upstream and downstream caspase activation, Poly ADP ribose polymerase cleavage and annexin V staining in MDA 686LN cells. Suppression of NF-κB by cell-permeable p65-based peptide and NBD peptide also inhibited the proliferation and induced apoptosis in these cells. Our results indicated that Curcumin is a potent inhibitor of cell proliferation and an inducer of apoptosis through suppression of IκB-alpha kinase-mediated NF-κB activation and of NF-κB-regulated gene expression.

Numerous reports suggested that interleukin-6 promotes survival and proliferation of tumor cells through the phosphorylation of a cell-signaling protein, STAT3. The constitutive activation of STAT3 in head and neck squamous cell carcinoma and its role in proliferation of this tumor has also been demonstrated. Thus, agents that can suppress STAT3 activation have potential for the treatment of head and neck squamous cell carcinoma. In the present report, we demonstrated that most head and neck squamous cell carcinoma cell lines had constitutively active STAT3 and Curcumin inhibited STAT3 phosphorylation in a dose and time-dependent manner [Chakravarti *et al.* 2006]. Nuclear translocation of STAT3 was also inhibited by Curcumin. Although the inhibition of STAT3 activation by Curcumin was reversible, only partial reversal occurred even after 24 h of Curcumin removal. Besides inhibiting constitutive expression, Curcumin also abrogated the interleukin-6-induced activation of STAT3 in head and neck squamous cell carcinoma cells. When compared with AG490, a well-characterized JAK2 inhibitor, Curcumin was more rapid (30 min vs. 4 h) and more potent (25 μM vs. 100 μM) inhibitor of STAT3 phosphorylation. Curcumin was also a more potent inhibitor of head and neck squamous cell carcinoma cell proliferation than AG490. Overall, our results demonstrated that Curcumin is a potent inhibitor of constitutive and interleukin-6-induced STAT3 phosphorylation. This mechanism may be at least partially responsible for Curcumin's ability to suppress proliferation of head and neck squamous cell carcinoma cells.

## Role of Curcumin in Oral Cancer

Smokeless tobacco (ST) consumption is a major cause of oral cancer in South East Asia including India. Recently, we showed that exposure to smokeless tobacco extract (STE) (khaini) resulted in increased expression and activation of NF-κB and its downstream target COX-2 in human oral cell systems *in vitro* [Sharma *et al.* 2006]. The present study was designed to test the hypothesis that Curcumin may inhibit the activation of NF-κB in smokeless tobacco exposed oral premalignant and cancer cells. Exposure of oral premalignant and cancer cells to Curcumin resulted in significant decrease in cell viability and induced apoptosis. Smokeless tobacco extract-induced nuclear translocation and DNA-binding activity of NF-κB were inhibited in Curcumin pretreated oral premalignant and cancer cells *in vitro*. Curcumin treatment led to decreased expression of NF-κB and COX-2. The tobacco specific nitrosamine, nicotine-derived nitrosamine ketone (NNK), is one of the carcinogenic components of smokeless tobacco extract (khaini). We demonstrate that Curcumin pretreatment abrogated NNK-induced activation of NF-κB and COX-2 expression, suggesting that NNK is one of the factors in smokeless tobacco extract (khaini) modulated by Curcumin. In conclusion, our findings demonstrated for the first time that Curcumin downregulates smokeless tobacco extract (khaini) or NNK-induced NF-κB and COX-2 in oral premalignant and cancer cells *in vitro.*

## Role of Curcumin in Ovarian Cancer

Curcumin has been shown to suppress inflammation and angiogenesis largely by inhibiting the transcription factor NF-κB. This study evaluated the effects of Curcumin (98% pure Curcumin from Sabinsa Corporation) on ovarian cancer growth using an orthotopic murine model of ovarian cancer [Lin *et al.* 2007]. *In vitro* and *in vivo* experiments of Curcumin with and without docetaxel were done using human ovarian cancer cell lines SKOV3ip1, HeyA8 and HeyA8-MDR in athymic mice. NF-κB modulation was ascertained using electrophoretic mobility shift assay. Evaluation of angiogenic cytokines, cellular proliferation (proliferating cell nuclear antigen), angiogenesis (CD31) and apoptosis (terminal deoxynucleotidyl transferase-mediated dUTP nick end labeling) were done using immunohistochemical analyses. Curcumin inhibited inducible NF-κB activation and suppressed proliferation *in vitro*. *In vivo* dose-finding experiments revealed that Curcumin suppressed NF-κB and STAT3 activation at a dose of 500 mg/kg, thereby decreasing the angiogenic cytokine expression. In the SKOV3ip1 and HeyA8 *in vivo* models, Curcumin alone resulted in 49% and 55% reductions in mean tumor growth compared with controls. When combined with docetaxel, Curcumin elicited 96% and 77% reductions in mean tumor growth compared with controls. In mice with multidrug-resistant HeyA8-MDR tumors, treatment with Curcumin alone and Curcumin + docetaxel combination resulted in significant reductions in tumor growth (47% and 58%, respectively). In SKOV3ip1 and HeyA8 tumors, Curcumin alone and Curcumin + docetaxel combination decreased both proliferation and microvessel density, and increased tumor cell apoptosis.

Based on significant efficacy in preclinical models, Curcumin-based therapies may be attractive in patients with ovarian carcinoma.

## Role of Curcumin in Breast Cancer

Pharmacologically safe compounds that can inhibit the proliferation of tumor cells have potential as anticancer agents. Curcumin exhibits anticarcinogenic properties *in vivo*. Curcumin suppressed c-jun/Ap-1 and NF-κB activation and type 1 human immunodeficiency virus long-terminal repeat-directed gene expression *in vitro*. We examined the antiproliferative effects of Curcumin against several breast tumor cell lines, including hormone-dependent and independent, and multidrug-resistant (MDR) lines [Mehta *et al.* 1997]. Cell growth inhibition was monitored by [3H]thymidine incorporation, trypan blue exclusion, crystal violet dye uptake and flow cytometry. All the cell lines tested including the MDR-positive ones were highly sensitive to Curcumin. The growth inhibitory effect of Curcumin was time and dose-dependent, and correlated with its inhibition of ornithine decarboxylase activity. Curcumin preferentially arrested cells in the G2/S phase of the cell cycle. Curcumin-induced cell death was neither due to apoptosis nor to any significant change in the expression of apoptosis-related genes including Bcl-2, p53, cyclin B and transglutaminase. Overall, our results suggested that Curcumin is a potent antiproliferative agent for breast tumor cells and may have potential as an anticancer agent.

Currently, there is no effective therapy for metastatic breast cancer after surgery, while radiation and chemotherapy have been used against the primary tumor. As most chemotherapeutic agents activate NF-κB that mediates cell survival, proliferation, invasion and metastasis, we hypothesized that Curcumin would potentiate the effect of chemotherapy in advanced breast cancer and inhibit lung metastasis by suppressing NF-κB activation. This hypothesis was validated using paclitaxel (Taxol)-resistant breast cancer cells and a human breast cancer xenograft model [Aggarwal *et al.* 2005]. The results indicated that Curcumin inhibited the paclitaxel-activated expression of NF-κB in breast cancer cells, as examined by electrophoretic mobility gel shift assay. This inhibition was mediated through inhibition of IκB-alpha kinase activation, IκB-alpha phosphorylation and degradation. Curcumin also suppressed the paclitaxel-induced expression of antiapoptotic, proliferative and metastatic proteins and also enhanced apoptosis. In a human breast cancer xenograft model, dietary administration of Curcumin significantly decreased the incidence of breast cancer metastasis to the lung and suppressed the expression of NF-κB, COX-2 and matrix metalloproteinase-9. Overall, our results indicated that Curcumin, which is a pharmacologically safe compound has a therapeutic potential in preventing breast cancer metastasis possibly through suppression of NF-κB and NF-κB-regulated gene products.

Success of cancer vaccination is strongly hampered by immune suppression in the tumor microenvironment (TME). Interleukin-6 is particularly and highly produced by triple-negative breast cancer (TNBC) cells and has been considered as an important contributor to immune suppression in the tumor microenvironment. Therefore, we hypothesized that interleukin-6 reduction may improve efficacy of vaccination against triple-negative breast cancer through improved T cell responses. To prove this hypothesis we investigated the effect of Curcumin, as an inhibitor of interleukin-6 production, on vaccination of a highly attenuated *Listeria monocytogenes* (Listeria(at)), encoding tumor-associated antigens (TAA) Mage-b in a triple-negative breast cancer model 4T1 [Singh *et al.* 2013]. Two therapeutic vaccination strategies with Listeria(at)-Mage-b and Curcumin were tested. The first immunization strategy involved all Listeria(at)-Mage-b vaccinations and Curcumin after tumor development. As Curcumin has been consumed all over the world, the second immunization strategy involved Curcumin before and all therapeutic vaccinations with Listeria(at)-Mage-b after tumor development. Here, we demonstrated that Curcumin significantly improved therapeutic efficacy of Listeria(at)-Mage-b with both immunization strategies particularly against metastases in a triple-negative breast cancer model (4T1). The combination therapy was slightly but significantly more effective against the metastases when Curcumin was administered before compared to after tumor development. When Curcumin administered before tumor development in combination therapy, the production of interleukin-6 was significantly decreased and interleukin-12 was increased by myeloid-derived suppressor cells (MDSC) with correlated improvement in CD4 and CD8 T cell responses in blood. Our study suggested that Curcumin improves the efficacy of Listeria(at)-Mage-b vaccine against metastases in triple-negative breast cancer model 4T1 through reversal of tumor-induced immune suppression.

 

## Role of Curcumin in Colon Cancer

The current treatment for advanced metastatic colorectal cancer (CRC) is ineffective because of the poor prognosis and the development of resistance against chemotherapeutic drugs. A study was carried out to understand whether Curcumin can potentiate the effect of capecitabine against growth and metastasis of colorectal cancer [Kunnumakkara *et al.* 2009]. The effect of Curcumin C3 Complex® on proliferation of colorectal cancer cell lines was examined by mitochondrial dye-uptake assay, apoptosis by esterase staining, NF-κB by electrophoretic mobility shift assay and gene expression by Western blot analysis. The effect of Curcumin on the growth and metastasis of colorectal cancer was also examined in orthotopically implanted tumors in nude mice. Curcumin inhibited the proliferation of human colorectal cancer cell lines, potentiated capecitabine-induced apoptosis, inhibited NF-κB activation and suppressed NF-κB-regulated gene products *in vitro*. In nude mice, the combination of Curcumin and capecitabine was found to be more effective than either agent alone in reducing tumor volume, Ki-67 proliferation index and microvessel density marker CD31. The combination treatment was also highly effective in suppressing ascites and distant metastasis to the liver, intestines, lungs, rectum and spleen. This effect was accompanied by suppressed expression of activated NF-κB and NF-κB-regulated gene products (cyclin D1,c-myc, bcl-2, bcl-xL, cIAP-1, COX-2, ICAM-1, matrix metallopeptidase-9, CXCR4 and vascular endothelial growth factor). Overall, our results suggested that Curcumin C3 Complex® sensitizes colorectal cancer to antitumor and antimetastatic effects of capecitabine by suppressing NF-κB cell signaling pathway.

## Role of Curcumin in Pancreatic Cancer

Pancreatic carcinoma is a lethal malignancy, with the best available therapeutic option gemcitabine-yielding response rates of < 10%. The transcription factor NF-κB is a potential therapeutic target because it has been determined to play a role in cell survival/proliferation in human pancreatic carcinoma. The authors investigated the ability of Curcumin to modulate NF-κB activity [Li *et al.* 2004]. Nuclear factor-κB and IκB kinase were constitutively active in all human pancreatic carcinoma cell lines examined and Curcumin consistently suppressed NF-κB binding (as assessed using an electrophoretic mobility gel-shift assay) and IκB kinase activity. Curcumin decreased the expression of NF-κB-regulated gene products including COX-2 (as assessed using immunoblot analysis), prostaglandin E2 and interleukin-8 (as assessed using an enzyme-linked immunoassay), all of which have been implicated in the growth and invasiveness of pancreatic carcinoma. These changes were associated with concentration and time-dependent antiproliferative activity (as assessed using a 3-[4,5-dimethylthiazol-2-yl]-2,5-diphenyltetrazolium bromide [MTT] assay) and pro-apoptotic effects (as assessed via annexin V/propidium iodide staining [fluorescence-activated cell sorting] as well as with the induction of polyadenosine-5'-diphosphate-ribose polymerase cleavage). Curcumin downregulated NF-κB and growth control molecules induced by NF-κB in human pancreatic cells. These effects were accompanied by marked growth inhibition and apoptosis. Through these findings authors provided a biologic rationale for the treatment of patients with pancreatic carcinoma using this non-toxic phytochemical.

Gemcitabine is currently the best treatment available for pancreatic cancer but the disease develops resistance to the drug over time. Agents that can either enhance the effects of gemcitabine or overcome chemoresistance to the drug are needed for the treatment of pancreatic cancer. Curcumin is one such agent that has been shown to suppress the transcription factor NF-κB, which is implicated in proliferation, survival, angiogenesis and chemoresistance. In this study, we investigated whether Curcumin C3 Complex® can sensitize pancreatic cancer to gemcitabine *in vitro* and *in vivo* [Kunnumakkara *et al.* 2007]. *In vitro,* Curcumin inhibited the proliferation of various pancreatic cancer cell lines, potentiated the apoptosis induced by gemcitabine and inhibited constitutive NF-κB activation in the cells. *In vivo,* nude mice injected with pancreatic cancer cells developed tumors that were treated with a combination of Curcumin C3 Complex® and gemcitabine. Results showed a significant reduction in volume, Ki-67 proliferation index, NF-κB activation and expression of NF-κB-regulated gene products compared with tumors from control mice treated with olive oil only. The combination treatment was also highly effective in suppressing angiogenesis as indicated by a decrease in CD31(+) microvessel density (P =

0.018 versus control). Overall, our results suggested that Curcumin potentiates the antitumor effects of gemcitabine in pancreatic cancer by suppressing proliferation, angiogenesis, NF-κB and NF-κB-regulated gene products.

## Clinical Study

Pancreatic cancer is almost always lethal and only gemcitabine and erlotinib are the USFDA-approved therapies for it, producing objective responses in <10% of patients. We evaluated the clinical/biological effects of Curcumin against advanced pancreatic cancer [Dhillon *et al.* 2008]. Patients received 8 g Curcumin by mouth daily until disease progression with restaging every 2 months. Curcumin was given in the form of 1 g caplets, each caplet containing 1 g Curcumin C3 Complex®. Serum cytokine levels for interleukin-6, interleukin-8, interleukin-10 and interleukin-1 receptor antagonists and peripheral blood mononuclear cell expression of NF-κB and COX-2 were monitored. Twenty-five patients were enrolled of which 21 met the inclusion criteria. Circulating Curcumin was detectable as drug in glucuronide and sulfate conjugate forms, albeit at low steady-state levels. Two patients showed clinical/ biological activity. One had ongoing stable disease for >18 months; interestingly, one additional patient had a brief, but marked tumor regression (73%) accompanied by significant (4 to 35-fold) increase in serum cytokine levels (interleukin-6, interleukin-8, interleukin-10, and interleukin-1 receptor antagonists). No toxicities were observed. Curcumin downregulated the expression of NF-κB, COX-2 and phosphorylated STAT3 in peripheral blood mononuclear cells from patients (most of whom had baseline levels considerably higher than those found in healthy volunteers). There was a considerable inter-patient variation in plasma Curcumin levels, where drug levels peaked at 22-41 ng/mL and remained relatively constant over the first 4 weeks. Oral Curcumin was well tolerated and despite its limited absorption, showed biological activity in patients with pancreatic cancer.

Curcumin could be a promising anticancer drug and shows synergic effects with cytotoxic agents. We evaluated the safety and feasibility of combination therapy using the patented composition of Curcumin C3 Complex® from Sabinsa with gemcitabine-based chemotherapy [Kanai *et al.* 2011]. Gemcitabine-resistant patients with pancreatic cancer received 8 g oral Curcumin C3 Complex® daily in combination with gemcitabine-based chemotherapy. The primary endpoint was safety for phase I and feasibility of oral Curcuminoids for phase II study. Twenty-one patients were enrolled. No dose-limiting toxicities were observed in the phase I study and oral Curcumin C3 Complex® 8 g/day was selected as the recommended dose for the phase II study. No patients were withdrawn from this study because of the intolerability of Curcuminoids, which met the primary endpoint of the phase II study and the median compliance rate of oral Curcumin was 100% (Range 79-100%). Median survival time after initiation of Curcumin C3 Complex® was 161 days (95% confidence interval 109-223 days) and one-year survival rate was 19% (4.4 to 41.4%). Plasma Curcumin levels ranged from 29-412 ng/mL in five patients tested. Combination therapy using 8 g oral Curcumin C3 Complex® daily with gemcitabine-based chemotherapy was safe and feasible in patients with pancreatic cancer and warrants further investigation into its efficacy.

## Role of Curcumin in Lung Cancer

Cigarette smoke (CS) is a major cause of a variety of malignancies including cancers of the larynx, oral cavity, pharynx, esophagus, pancreas, kidney, bladder and lung. The signal transduction pathway that mediates the effects of cigarette smoke is not well understood but NF-κB is probably involved. The gas phase of cigarette smoke contains free radicals such as superoxide radicals, hydroxyl radicals and hydrogen peroxide, which potentially can activate NF-κB. Benzo[a]pyrene, another potent carcinogen of cigarette smoke, can also activate NF-κB but by an as yet unknown mechanism. Various other agents that activate NF-κB are either tumor initiators or tumor promoters and NF-κB activation can block apoptosis, promote proliferation and mediate tumorigenesis. Therefore, NF-κB is an ideal target for preventing cigarette smoke-induced lung carcinogenesis. Thus, agents that abrogate NF-κB activation have the potential to suppress lung carcinogenesis. Since Curcumin is an anticarcinogenic, we investigated the effect of this phytochemical on cigarette smoke-induced NF-κB activation and NF-κB-regulated gene expression in human non-small cell lung carcinoma cells [Shishodia *et al.* 2003]. Exposure of cells to cigarette smoke induced persistent activation of NF-κB and pre-treatment with Curcumin abolished the cigarette smoke-induced DNA-binding of NF-κB, IκB-alpha kinase activation, IκB-alpha phosphorylation and degradation, p65 nuclear translocation and cigarette smoke-induced NF-κB-dependent reporter gene expression. The inhibition of NF-κB activation correlated with suppression of cigarette smoke-induced NF-κB-dependent cyclin D1, COX-2 and matrix metalloproteinase-9 expression. Overall, our results indicated that cigarette smoke-induced NF-κB activation and NF-κB-regulated gene expression in human non-small cell lung carcinoma cells was suppressed by Curcumin through suppression of IκB-alpha kinase.

Recent studies have demonstrated that K-ras mutations in lung epithelial cells elicit inflammation that promotes carcinogenesis in mice (intrinsic inflammation). The finding that patients with chronic obstructive pulmonary disease (COPD), an inflammatory disease of the lung, have an increased risk of lung cancer after controlling for smoking suggests a further link between lung cancer and extrinsic inflammation. Besides exposure to cigarette smoke, it is thought that airway inflammation in chronic obstructive pulmonary disease is caused by bacterial colonization, particularly with non-typeable hemophilus influenzae (NTHi). Previously, we have shown that non-typeable hemophilus influenzae-induced chronic obstructive pulmonary disease-like airway inflammation promotes lung cancer in an airway conditional K-ras-induced mouse model. To further test the role of inflammation in cancer promotion, we administered Curcumin 1% in diet before and during weekly non-typeable hemophilus influenzae exposure [Moghaddam *et al.* 2009]. This significantly reduced the number of visible lung tumors in the absence of non-typeable hemophilus influenzae exposure by 85% and in the presence of non-typeable hemophilus influenzae exposures by 53%. Mechanistically, Curcumin markedly suppressed non-typeable hemophilus influenzae-induced increased levels of the neutrophil chemoattractant keratinocyte-derived chemokine by 80% and neutrophils by 87% in bronchoalveolar lavage fluid. *In vitro* studies of murine K-ras-induced lung adenocarcinoma cell lines (LKR-10 and LKR-13) indicated direct antitumor effects of Curcumin by reducing cell viability, colony formation and inducing apoptosis. We concluded that Curcumin suppressed the progression of K-ras-induced lung cancer in mice by inhibiting intrinsic and extrinsic inflammation, and by direct antitumor effects. These findings suggested that Curcumin could be used to protract the premalignant phase and inhibit lung cancer progression in high-risk chronic obstructive pulmonary disease patients.

## Role of Curcumin in Gall Bladder Cancer

Cholangiocarcinoma (CCA) is a tumor with poor prognosis that is resistant to all currently available treatments. The potential therapeutic activity of Curcumin against human cholangiocarcinoma was investigated using three cholangiocarcinoma cell lines (KKU100, KKU-M156 and KKU-M213) [Prakobwong *et al.* 2011a]. Examination of mitochondrial dehydrogenase activity, phosphatidylserine externalization, esterase staining, caspase activation and poly-adenosine diphosphate ribose polymerase cleavage demonstrated that Curcumin inhibited proliferation of biliary cancer cells and induced apoptosis in these cells. Colony-formation assay confirmed the growth-inhibitory effect of Curcumin on cholangiocarcinoma cells. When examined for the mechanism, 98% pure Curcumin from Sabinsa Corporation was found to activate multiple cell signaling pathways in these cells. First, all cholangiocarcinoma cells exhibited constitutively active NF-κB and treatment with Curcumin abolished this activation as indicated by DNA binding, nuclear translocation and p65 phosphorylation. Second, Curcumin suppressed activation of STAT3 as indicated by decreased phosphorylation at both tyrosine 705 and serine 727 and inhibition of janus kinase-1 phosphorylation. Third, Curcumin induced expression of peroxisome proliferator-activated receptor gamma. Fourth, Curcumin upregulated death receptors DR4 and DR5. Fifth, Curcumin suppressed the Akt activation pathway. Sixth, Curcumin inhibited expression of cell survival proteins such as B-cell lymphoma-2, B-cell leukemia protein xL, X-linked inhibitor of apoptosis protein, c-FLIP, cellular inhibitor of apoptosis protein (cIAP)-1, cIAP-2 and survivin and proteins linked to cell proliferation such as cyclin D1 and c-Myc.

Seventh, the growth inhibitory effect of Curcumin was enhanced in the IκB kinase-deficient cells, the enzyme required for NFκB activation. Overall, our results indicated that Curcumin mediates its antiproliferative and apoptotic effects through activation of multiple cell signaling pathways and thus, its activity against cholangiocarcinoma should be further investigated.

Cholangiocarcinoma is a highly metastatic tumor linked to liver fluke infection. Consumption of nitrosamine-contaminated foods is a major health problem especially in South-Eastern Asia. In search for a suitable chemopreventive agents, we investigated the effect of Curcumin on cholangiocarcinoma development in an animal model by infection with the liver fluke *Opisthorchis viverrini* and administration of N-nitrosodimethylamine and fed with Curcumin-supplemented diet [Prakobwong *et al.* 2011b]. The effect of Curcumin-supplemented diet on histopathological changes and survival were assessed in relation to NF-κB activation and the expression of NF-κB-related gene products involved in inflammation, DNA damage, apoptosis, cell proliferation, angiogenesis and metastasis. Our results showed that dietary administration of this nutraceutical significantly reduced the incidence of cholangiocarcinoma and increased the survival of animals. This correlated with the suppression of the activation of transcription factors including NF-κB, AP-1 and STAT3, and reduction in the expression of pro-inflammatory proteins such as COX-2 and inducible nitric oxide synthase. The formation of inducible nitric oxide synthase-dependent DNA lesions (8-nitroguanine and 8-oxo-7,8-dihydro-2'-deoxyguanosine) was inhibited. Curcumin suppressed the expression of proteins related to cell survival (bcl-2 and bcl-xL), proliferation (cyclin D1 and c-myc), tumor invasion (matrix metallopeptidase-9 and ICAM-1), angiogenesis (vascular endothelial growth factor) and microvessel density. Induction of apoptotic events as indicated by caspase activation and Poly (ADP) ribose polymerase cleavage was also noted. Our results suggested that Curcumin exhibits an anticarcinogenic potential via suppression of various events involved in multiple steps of carcinogenesis, which is accounted for by its ability to suppress pro-inflammatory pathways.

## Role of Curcumin in Bladder Cancer

Bladder cancer mortality varies between the countries; whereas being highest in Western countries and lowest in Eastern countries, such as India. Cigarette smoking is one of the major risk factors for bladder cancer in affluent nations such as the United States. Localized early-stage bladder cancer is treated with resection and intravesical cytokine therapy, whereas metastatic cancer is typically treated with various combinations of systemic chemotherapy. The role of Curcumin in prevention and treatment of bladder cancer was investigated [Kamat *et al.* 2007]. We found that 98% Curcumin supplied by Sabinsa Corporation inhibited the proliferation, induced cell cycle arrest and DNA fragmentation in both interferon-α-sensitive (RT4V6) and interferon-α-resistant (KU-7) bladder cancer cells. Curcumin also potentiated the apoptotic effects of the chemotherapeutic agents (gemcitabine and paclitaxel) and of cytokines (TNF-α and TNF-α-related apoptosis-inducing ligand). This effect of Curcumin was independent of sensitivity and resistance to interferon-α, commonly used for treatment of bladder cancer. The effects of Curcumin mediated through modulation of the NF-κB pathway known to mediate antiapoptosis were also investigated. Both gemcitabine and TNF-α-activated NF-κB in bladder cancer cells and Curcumin suppressed this activation. Similarly, cigarette smoke also activated NF-κB and Curcumin suppressed it. Cigarette smoke-induced expression of the NF-κB-regulated gene products COX-2 and vascular endothelial growth factor, linked with proliferation and angiogenesis, respectively, were also downregulated by Curcumin.

Eventual failure of response to Bacillus Calmette-Guerin (BCG) intravesical therapy, a standard treatment for bladder cancer, is a major problem. Treatments that can augment Bacillus Calmette-Guerin therapy are urgently needed. We investigated whether Curcumin has the potential to improve the current therapy using *in vitro* and *in vivo* MBT-2 murine tumor models [Kamat *et al.* 2009]. We found that Curcumin potentiated Bacillus Calmette-Guerin-induced apoptosis of human bladder cancer cells. Bacillus Calmette-Guerin stimulated the release of TNF-α-related apoptosis-inducing ligand (TRAIL) from peripheral mononuclear neutrophils in a dose and time-dependent manner, whereas Curcumin enhanced the upregulation of TRAIL receptors. Electrophoretic mobility shift assay revealed that Curcumin also suppressed the Bacillus Calmette-Guerin-induced activation of the cell survival transcription factor NF-κB. In a syngeneic bladder cancer model, Curcumin alone reduced the bladder tumor volume but a significantly greater reduction was observed when Bacillus Calmette-Guerin and Curcumin were used in combination. This was accompanied by a significant decrease in the proliferation marker Ki-67 and microvessel density (CD31), decreased NF-κB in tumor tissue compared with the control, induced apoptosis and decreased cyclin D1, vascular endothelial growth factor, COX-2, c-myc and Bcl-2 expression in the tumor tissue. Upregulation of TRAIL receptor by the combination was also observed in tumor tissues. Overall, our results suggested that Curcumin potentiates the antitumor effect of Bacillus Calmette-Guerin through inhibition of NF-κB and induction of TRAIL receptors in bladder cancer cells.

Little progress has been made in the last three decades in the treatment of bladder cancer. Novel agents that are non-toxic and can improve the current standard of care of this disease are urgently needed. Curcumin is one such agent that has been shown to suppress pathways linked to oncogenesis including cell survival, proliferation, invasion and angiogenesis [Tharakan *et al.* 2010]. We investigated whether Curcumin C3 Complex® has potential to improve the current therapy for bladder cancer using an orthotopic mouse model. Curcumin C3 Complex® potentiated the apoptotic effects of gemcitabine against human bladder cancer 253JBV cells in culture. Electrophoretic mobility shift assay revealed that Curcumin also suppressed the gemcitabine-induced activation of the cell survival transcription factor NF-κB. In an orthotopic mouse model, bioluminescence imaging revealed that while Curcumin C3 Complex® alone significantly reduced the bladder tumor volume, maximum reduction was observed when Curcumin was used in combination with gemcitabine. Curcumin also significantly decreased the proliferation marker Ki-67 and microvessel density (CD31) but maximum reduction occurred when it was combined with gemcitabine. Curcumin abolished the constitutive activation of NF-κB in the tumor tissue; induced apoptosis, decreased cyclin D1, vascular endothelial growth factor, COX-2, c-myc and Bcl-2 expression in the bladder cancer tissue. Overall, our results suggested that Curcumin C3 Complex® alone exhibits significant antitumor effects against human bladder cancer and it further potentiates the effects of gemictabine, possibly through the modulation of NF-κB signaling pathway.

## Role of Curcumin in Prostate Cancer

While the role of nuclear transcription factor activator protein-1 (AP-1) in cell proliferation and of NF-κB in the suppression of apoptosis are known, their role in survival of prostate cancer cells is not well understood [Mukhopadhyay *et al.* 2001]. We investigated the role of NF-κB and AP-1 in the survival of human androgen-independent (DU145) and dependent (LNCaP) prostate cancer cell lines. Our results showed that the faster rate of proliferation of DU145 cells when compared to LNCaP cells correlated with the constitutive expression of activated NF-κB and AP-1 in DU-145 cells. In DU145 cells both c-Fos and c-Jun were expressed and treatment with TNF-α-activated c-Jun NH2-terminal kinase (JNK), needed for AP-1 activation. In LNCaP cells, however, only low levels of c-Jun was expressed and treatment with Curcumin suppressed both constitutive (DU145) and inducible (LNCaP) NF-κB activation and potentiated TNF-α-induced apoptosis. Curcumin alone induced apoptosis in both cell types, which correlated with the downregulation of the expression of Bcl-2 and Bcl-xL and the activation of procaspase-3 and procaspase-8. Overall, our results suggested that NF-κB and AP-1 may play a role in the survival of prostate cancer cells and Curcumin abrogates their survival mechanisms.

## Role of Curcumin in Cutaneous T cell Lymphoma

Curcumin is reported to inhibit cell growth and induce apoptosis in a number of tumor cell lines and animal models. Human clinical trials indicated no dose-limiting toxicity when administered at doses up to 8 g per day. The purpose of this study was to address the antitumor effect of Curcumin on cutaneous T cell lymphoma (CTCL) cell lines and peripheral blood mononuclear cells from patients with cutaneous T cell lymphoma compared with healthy donors controls [Zhang *et al.* 2010]. Curcumin at 5-20 μM for 24 and

48 h induced apoptosis in a time and dose-dependent manner in three cutaneous T cell lymphoma cell lines (namely MJ, Hut78 and HH). Curcumin at 5-20 μM for 48 h also caused more apoptosis in patients peripheral blood mononuclear cells compared with healthy donors peripheral blood mononuclear cells ($P<0.05$). Curcumin decreased protein and mRNA expression levels of STAT3, bcl-2 and survivin in three cell lines, and in patients' peripheral blood mononuclear cells. Curcumin inhibited STAT3 and IκB-alpha phosphorylation as well as suppressed DNA binding of NFκB in these cells. Caspase-3 was activated and poly ADP-ribose polymerase was cleaved after Curcumin treatment. These results suggested that Curcumin selectively induces apoptosis in association with the downregulation of STAT3 and NF-κB signaling pathways in cutaneous T cell lymphoma cells. Our findings provided a mechanistic rationale for the potential use of Curcumin as a therapeutic agent for patients with cutaneous T cell lymphoma.

## Mantle Cell Lymphoma

Human mantle cell lymphoma (MCL), an aggressive B cell Non-Hodgkin's lymphoma, is characterized by the overexpression of cyclin D1, which plays an essential role in the survival and proliferation of mantle cell lymphoma. Due to the development of resistance of mantle cell lymphoma to current chemotherapy, novel approaches are needed for effective treatment and therapy. Since mantle cell lymphoma cells are known to over express NF-κB-regulated gene products (including cyclin D1), we used Curcumin to target NF-κB in a variety of mantle cell lymphoma cell lines. All four mantle cell lymphoma cell lines examined had overexpression of cyclin D1, constitutive active NF-κB and IκB kinase, and phosphorylated forms of IκB-alpha and p65. This correlated with expression of TNF-α, IκB-alpha, Bcl-2, Bcl-xL, COX-2 and interleukin-6, all regulated by NF-κB. Treatment of cells with Curcumin, however, downregulated constitutive active NF-κB and inhibited the consitutively active IκB-alpha kinase and phosphorylation of IκB-alpha and p65. Curcumin also inhibited constitutive activation of Akt, needed for IκB-alpha kinase activation [Shishodia *et al.* 2005]. Consequently, the expression of all NF-κB-regulated gene products were downregulated by the polyphenol leading to the suppression of proliferation, cell cycle arrest at the G1/S phase of the cell cycle and induction of apoptosis (as indicated by caspase activation), poly ADP ribose polymerase cleavage and annexin V staining. The fact that NF-κB activation is directly linked to the proliferation of cells was also indicated by the observation that peptide derived from the IKK/NEMO-binding domain and p65 suppressed the constitutive active NF-κB complex and inhibited the proliferation of MCL cells. Constitutive NF-κB activation was found to be due to TNF-α, as anti-TNF-α antibodies inhibited both NF-κB activation and proliferation of cells. Overall, our results indicated that Curcumin inhibits the constitutive NF-κB and IκB-alpha kinase leading to suppression of expression of NF-κB-regulated gene products. This inturn results in the suppression of proliferation, cell cycle arrest and induction of apoptosis in mantle cell lymphoma.

## Melanoma

Nuclear factor-κB plays a central role in cell survival and proliferation in human melanoma. Therefore, the authors explored the possibility of exploiting NF-κB for melanoma treatment by using Curcumin, a potent NF-κB-inhibitor with little toxicity in humans [Siwak *et al.* 2005]. Three melanoma cell lines (C32, G-361, and WM 266-4) all of which had B-raf mutations were treated with Curcumin. The authors assessed its effects on viability ((3-[4,5-dimethylthiazol-2-yl]2,5-diphenyltetrazolium bromide assay) and apoptosis (flow-cytometric analysis of annexin V/propidium iodide-stained cells). Curcumin-treated cells were also examined for NF-κB binding activity (electrophoretic mobility shift assay) and for the activity of its upstream regulator, IκB kinase (immune complex kinase assay). In addition, relevant signalling as reflected by B-Raf kinase activity (kinase cascade assay) and steady-state levels of activated downstream effectors as reflected by mitogen-activated signal-regulated protein kinase (MEK), extracellular signal-regulated protein kinase (ERK) and Akt phosphorylation levels (immunoblots) were assessed. Curcumin treatment decreased cell viability of all 3 cell lines in a dose-dependent manner (50% inhibitory concentration = 6.1-7.7 μM) and induced apoptosis. Nuclear factor-κB and IκB-alpha kinase were active constitutively in all melanoma cell lines examined. Curcumin under apoptosis-inducing conditions downregulated NF-κB and IκB-alpha kinase activities. However, Curcumin did not inhibit the activities of B-Raf, mitogen-activated signal-regulated protein kinase or extracellular signal-regulated protein kinase and Akt phosphorylation was enhanced. Furthermore, in the presence of Curcumin, the Akt inhibitor 1L-6-hydroxymethyl-chiro-inositol 2-[(R)-2-O-methyl-3-O-octadecylcarbonate] no longer suppressed Akt phosphorylation. Curcumin has potent antiproliferative and pro-apoptotic effects in melanoma cells. These effects were associated with the suppression of NF-κB and IκB-alpha kinase activities but were independent of the B-Raf/MEK/ERK and Akt pathways.

## Brain Cancer

Autophagy is a response of cancer cells to various anticancer therapies. It is designated as programmed cell death type II and characterized by the formation of autophagic vacuoles in the cytoplasm. The Akt/mammalian target of rapamycin (mTOR)/p70 ribosomal protein S6 kinase (p70S6K) and the extracellular signal-regulated kinases 1/2 (ERK1/2) pathways are two major pathways that regulate autophagy induced by nutrient starvation. These pathways are also frequently associated with oncogenesis in a variety of cancer cell types including malignant gliomas. However, few studies have examined both of these signal pathways in the context of anticancer therapy-induced autophagy in cancer cells and the effect of autophagy on cell death remains unclear. Here, we examined the anticancer efficacy and mechanisms of Curcumin in U87-MG and U373-MG malignant glioma cells [Aoki *et al.* 2007). Curcumin (95% pure; supplied by Sabinsa) induced G(2)/M arrest and nonapoptotic autophagic cell death in both cell types. It inhibited the Akt/mTOR/p70S6K pathway and activated the ERK1/2 pathway, resulting in induction of autophagy. It is interesting that activation of the Akt pathway inhibited Curcumin-induced autophagy and cytotoxicity, whereas inhibition of the ERK1/2 pathway inhibited Curcumin-induced autophagy and induced apoptosis, thus resulting in enhanced cytotoxicity. These results imply that the effect of autophagy on cell death may be pathway-specific. In the subcutaneous xenograft model of U87-MG cells Curcumin inhibited tumor growth significantly and induced autophagy. These results suggested that Curcumin has high anticancer efficacy *in vitro* and *in vivo* by inducing autophagy and warrant further investigation towards possible clinical application in patients with malignant glioma.

# *Curcumin for Bone Loss*

Numerous studies have indicated that inflammatory cytokines play a major role in osteoclastogenesis leading to the bone resorption that is frequently associated with cancer and other diseases. Gene deletion studies have shown that receptor activator of NF-κB ligand (RANKL) is one of the critical mediators of osteoclastogenesis. How RANKL mediates osteoclastogenesis is not fully understood but an agent that suppresses RANKL signaling has potential to inhibit osteoclastogenesis. In this report, we examined the ability of Curcumin to suppress RANKL signaling and osteoclastogenesis in RAW 264.7 cells, a murine monocytic cell line [Bharti *et al.* 2004b]. Treatment of these cells with RANKL-activated NF-κB and pre-exposure of the cells to Curcumin completely suppressed RANKL-induced NF-κB activation. Curcumin inhibited the pathway leading from activation of IκB-alpha kinase and IκB-alpha phosphorylation to IκB-alpha degradation. RANKL-induced osteoclastogenesis in these monocytic cells and Curcumin inhibited both RANKL and TNF-α-induced osteoclastogenesis and pit formation. Curcumin suppressed osteoclastogenesis maximally when added together with RANKL and minimally when it was added 2 days after RANKL. Curcumin's ability to inhibit RANKL-induced osteoclastogenesis through suppression of NF-κB was also confirmed independently as RANKL failed to activate NF-κB in cells stably transfected with a dominant-negative form of IκB-alpha and concurrently failed to induce osteoclastogenesis. Thus, overall these results indicated that RANKL induces osteoclastogenesis through the activation of NF-κB and treatment with Curcumin inhibits both the NF-κB activation and osteoclastogenesis induced by RANKL.

# *Delivery System for Curcumin*

Curcumin has been linked with antioxidant, anti-inflammatory, antiproliferative, anticancer, antidiabetic, antirheumatic and antiviral effects. However, its optimum potential is limited by its lack of solubility in aqueous solvents and poor oral bioavailability. We employed a polymer-based nanoparticle approach to improve the bioavailability [Anand *et al.* 2010]. Curcumin C3 Complex® provided by Sabinsa was encapsulated with 97.5% efficiency in biodegradable nanoparticulate formulation based on poly(lactic-co-glycolic acid) (PLGA) and a stabilizer polyethylene glycol (PEG)-5000. Dynamic laser light scattering and transmission electron microscopy indicated a particle diameter of 80.9 nm. This Curcumin, renamed from hereon as "Curcumin (NP)" was characterized for its biological activity. *In vitro* Curcumin (NP) exhibited very rapid and more efficient cellular uptake than Curcumin. Estrase staining revealed that Curcumin (NP) was at least as potent as or more potent than Curcumin in inducing apoptosis of leukemic cells and in suppressing proliferation of various tumor cell lines. In mice, Curcumin (NP) was more bioavailable and had a longer half-life than Curcumin. Overall, we demonstrated that Curcumin-loaded PLGA nanoparticles formulation has enhanced cellular uptake and increased bioactivity *in vitro* and superior bioavailability *in vivo* over Curcumin.

Although Curcumin has been linked with multiple beneficial activities, its optimum potential is limited by poor bioavailability, in part due to the lack of solubility in aqueous solvents. To overcome the solubility problem, a novel cyclodextrin complex of Curcumin was developed and examined for its anti-inflammatory and antiproliferative effects [Yadav *et al.* 2010]. Curcumin C3 Complex® was used to prepare the cyclodextrin complex for the study. As evidenced from the electrophoretic mobility shift assay, cyclodextrin complex of Curcumin was observed to be more active than free Curcumin in inhibiting TNF-α-induced activation of the inflammatory transcription factor NF-κB and in suppressing gene products regulated by NF-κB including those involved in cell proliferation (cyclin D1), invasion (matrix metallopeptidase-9) and angiogenesis (vascular endothelial growth factor). Cyclodextrin complex of Curcumin was also more active than free Curcumin in inducing the death receptors DR4 and DR5. Annexin V staining, cleavage of caspase-3 and Poly ADP ribose polymerase, DNA fragmentation showed that cyclodextrin complex of Curcumin was more potent than free Curcumin in inducing apoptosis of leukemic cells. Antiproliferative assays also demonstrated that cyclodextrin complex of Curcumin was more active than free Curcumin in suppressing proliferation of various cancer cell lines. The cyclodextrin vehicle had no effect in these assays. Compared with free Curcumin, cyclodextrin complex of Curcumin had a greater cellular uptake and longer half-life in the cells. Overall, we demonstrated that cyclodextrin complex of Curcumin had superior attributes compared with free Curcumin for cellular uptake and for antiproliferative and anti-inflammatory activities.

Biologically derived nanoparticles (<100 nm) were fabricated for local and sustained therapeutic Curcumin delivery to cancer cells. Silk fibroin and chitosan polymers were blended noncovalently to encapsulate Curcumin in various proportions of silk fibroin and chitosan (75:25, 50:50 and 25:75 Silk fibroin:chitosan) or pure silk fibroin at two concentrations (0.1% w/v and 10% w/v) using the devised capillary-microdot technique [Gupta *et al.* 2009]. Curcumin-polymer conjugates were frozen, lyophilized, crystallized, suspended in phosphate-buffered saline for characterization and tested for efficacy against breast cancer cells. All nanoparticle formulations except 0.1% w/v 50:50 silk fibroin and chitosan were less than 100 nm in size as determined with the transmission electron microscopy. The entrapment and release of Curcumin over eight days was highest for silk fibroin-derived nanoparticles as compared to all silk fibroin and chitosan blends. The uptake and efficacy of silk fibroin-coated Curcumin was significantly higher ($p < 0.001$) than silk fibroin and chitosan-coated Curcumin in both low and high Her2/neu expressing breast cancer cells. Interestingly, the uptake of Curcumin was highest for the high Her2/neu expressing breast cancer cells when delivered with a 10% w/v silk fibroin coating as compared to other formulations. In conclusion, silk fibroin-derived Curcumin nanoparticles showed higher efficacy against breast cancer cells and have the potential to treat *in vivo* breast tumors by local, sustained and long-term therapeutic delivery as a biodegradable system.

# *Conclusion*

Overall, all these studies from our group indicate that the Curcumin derived from golden spice exhibits multiple biological activites. It is a multi-targeted agent that is highly safe and thus, should be explored further in the clinic.

# References


Aggarwal BB, Kumar A, Bharti AC. Anticancer potential of Curcumin: preclinical and clinical studies. *Anticancer Res*. 2003;23(1A):363-98.

Aggarwal BB, Shishodia S, Takada Y, Banerjee S, Newman RA, Bueso-Ramos CE, Price JE. Curcumin suppresses the paclitaxel-induced nuclear factor-κB pathway in breast cancer cells and inhibits lung metastasis of human breast cancer in nude mice. *Clin Cancer Res*. 2005;11(20):7490-98.

Aggarwal BB, Sundaram C, Malani N, Ichikawa H. Curcumin: The Indian solid gold. *Adv Exp Med Biol*. 2007;595:1-75.

Aggarwal BB, Gupta SC, Sung B. Curcumin: an orally bioavailable blocker of TNF and other proinflammatory biomarkers. *Br J Pharmacol*. 2013;169(8):1672-92.

Aggarwal BB, Deb L, Prasad S. Curcumin differs from tetrahydrocurcumin for molecular targets, signalling pathways and cellular responses. *Molecules*. 2014;20(1):185-205.

Aggarwal S, Takada Y, Singh S, Myers JN, Aggarwal BB. Inhibition of growth and survival of human head and neck squamous cell carcinoma cells by Curcumin via modulation of nuclear factor-κB signaling. Int J Cancer. 2004;111(5):679-92. Erratum in: *Int J Cancer*. 2004;112(6):1086.

Anand P, Thomas SG, Kunnumakkara AB, Sundaram C, Harikumar KB, Sung B, Tharakan ST, Misra K, Priyadarsini IK, Rajasekharan KN, Aggarwal BB. Biological activities of Curcumin and its analogues (Congeners) made by man and Mother Nature. *Biochem Pharmacol*. 2008;76(11):1590-611.

Anand P, Nair HB, Sung B, KunnumakkaraAB, Yadav VR, Tekmal RR, Aggarwal BB. Design of Curcumin loaded PLGA nanoparticles formulation with enhanced cellular uptake, and increased bioactivity in vitro and superior bioavailability in vivo. *Biochem Pharmacol*. 2010; 79(3):330-38.

Anand P, Sung B, Kunnumakkara AB, Rajasekharan KN, Aggarwal BB. Suppression of pro-inflammatory and proliferative pathways by diferuloylmethane (Curcumin) and its analogues dibenzoylmethane, dibenzoylpropane, and dibenzylideneacetone: role of Michael acceptors and Michael donors. *Biochem Pharmacol*. 2011; 82(12):1901-09.

Anto RJ, Mukhopadhyay A, Denning K, Aggarwal BB. Curcumin (diferuloylmethane) induces apoptosis through activation of caspase-8, BID cleavage and cytochrome c release: its suppression by ectopic expression of Bcl-2 and Bcl-xl. *Carcinogenesis*. 2002;23(1):143-50.

Anthwal A, Thakur BK, Rawat MS, Rawat DS, Tyagi AK, Aggarwal BB. Synthesis, characterization and in vitro anticancer activity of C-5 Curcumin analogues with potential to inhibit TNF-α-induced NF-κB activation. *Biomed Res Int*. 2014. DOI: 10.1155/2014/524161

Aoki H, Takada Y, Kondo S, Sawaya R, Aggarwal BB, Kondo Y. Evidence that Curcumin suppresses the growth of malignant gliomas in vitro and in vivo through induction of autophagy: role of Akt and extracellular signal-regulated kinase signaling pathways. *Mol Pharmacol*. 2007;72(1):29-39.

Bharti AC, Donato N, Aggarwal BB. Curcumin (diferuloylmethane) inhibits constitutive and IL-6-inducible STAT3 phosphorylation in human multiple myeloma cells. *J Immunol*. 2003a;171(7):3863-71.

Bharti AC, Donato N, Singh S, Aggarwal BB. Curcumin (diferuloylmethane) down-regulates the constitutive activation of nuclear factor-κB and IκBalpha kinase in human multiple myeloma cells, leading to suppression of proliferation and induction of apoptosis. *Blood*. 2003b;101(3):1053-62.

Bharti AC, Shishodia S, Reuben JM, Weber D, Alexanian R. Raj-Vadhan S, Estrov Z, Talpaz M, Aggarwal BB. Nuclear factor-κB and STAT3 are constitutively active in CD138+ cells derived from multiple myeloma patients, and suppression of these transcription factors leads to apoptosis. *Blood*. 2004a;103(8):3175-84.

Bharti AC, Takada Y, Aggarwal BB. Curcumin (diferuloylmethane) inhibits receptor activator of NF-κB ligand-induced NF-κB activation in osteoclast precursors and suppresses osteoclastogenesis. *J Immunol*. 2004b; 172(10):5940-47.

Chakravarti N, Myers JN, Aggarwal BB. Targeting constitutive and interleukin-6-inducible signal transducers and activators of transcription 3 pathway in head and neck squamous cell carcinoma cells by Curcumin (diferuloylmethane). *Int J Cancer*. 2006;119(6):1268-75.

Dhillon N, Aggarwal BB, Newman RA, Wolff RA, Kunnumakkara AB, Abbruzzese JL, Ng CS, Badmaev V, Kurzrock R. Phase II trial of Curcumin in patients with advanced pancreatic cancer. *Clin Cancer Res*. 2008;14(14):4491-99.

Goel A and Aggarwal BB. Curcumin, the golden spice from Indian saffron, is a chemosensitizer and radiosensitizer for tumors and chemoprotector and radioprotector for normal organs. *Nutr Cancer*. 2010;62(7):919-30.

Gupta V, Aseh A, Rios CN, Aggarwal BB, Mathur AB. Fabrication and characterization of silk fibroin-derived Curcumin nanoparticles for cancer therapy. *Int J Nanomedicine*. 2009;4:115-22.

Jagetia GC and Aggarwal BB. "Spicing up" of the immune system by Curcumin. *J Clin Immunol*. 2007;27(1):19-35.

Kamat AM, Sethi G, Aggarwal BB. Curcumin potentiates the apoptotic effects of chemotherapeutic agents and cytokines through down-regulation of nuclear factor-κB and nuclear factor-κB-regulated gene products in IFN-alpha-sensitive and IFN-alpha-resistant human bladder cancer cells. *Mol Cancer Ther*. 2007;6(3):1022-30.

Kamat AM, Tharakan ST, Sung B, Aggarwal BB. Curcumin potentiates the antitumor effects of Bacillus Calmette-Guerin against bladder cancer through the downregulation of NF-κB and upregulation of TRAIL receptors. *Cancer Res*. 2009;69(23):8958-66.

 

Kanai M, Yoshimura K, Asada M, Imaizumi A, Suzuki C, Matsumoto S, Nishimura T, Mori Y, Masui T, Kawaguchi Y, Yanagihara K, Yazumi S, Chiba T, Guha S, Aggarwal BB. A phase I/II study of gemcitabine based chemotherapy plus Curcumin for patients with gemcitabine-resistant pancreatic cancer. *Cancer Chemother Pharmacol.* 2011;68(1):157-64.

Kumar A, Dhawan S, Hardegen NJ, Aggarwal BB. Curcumin (Diferuloylmethane) inhibition of tumor necrosis factor (TNF)-mediated adhesion of monocytes to endothelial cells by suppression of cell surface expression of adhesion molecules and of nuclear factor-κB activation. *Biochem Pharmacal.* 1998;55(6):775-83.

Kunnumakkara AB, Guha S, Krishnan S, Diagaradjane P, Gelovani J, Aggarwal BB. Curcumin potentiates antitumor activity of gemcitabine in an orthotopic model of pancreatic cancer through suppression of proliferation, angiogenesis, and inhibition of nuclear factor-κB-regulated gene products. *Cancer Res.* 2007;67(8):3853-61.

Kunnumakkara AB, Anand P, Aggarwal BB. Curcumin inhibits proliferation, invasion, angiogenesis and metastasis of different cancers through interaction with multiple cell signaling proteins. *Cancer Lett.* 2008;269(2):199-225.

Kunnumakkara AB, Diagaradjane P, Anand P, Harikumar KB, Deorukhkar A, Gelovani J, Guha S, Krishnan S, Aggarwal BB. Curcumin sensitizes human colorectal cancer to capecitabine by modulation of cyclin D1, COX-2, MMP-9, VEGF and CXCR4 expression in an orthotopic mouse model. *Int J Cancer.* 2009;125(9):2187-97.

Li L, Aggarwal BB, Shishodia S, Abbruzzese J, Kurzrock R. Nuclear factor-κB and IκB kinase are constitutively active in human pancreatic cells, and their down-regulation by Curcumin (diferuloylmethane) is associated with the suppression of proliferation and the induction of apoptosis. *Cancer.* 2004;101(10):2351-62.

Lin YG, Kunnumakkara AB, Nair A, Merritt WM, Han LY, Armaiz-Pena GN, Kamat AA, Spannuth WA, Gershenson DM, Lutgendorf SK. Aggarwal BB, Sood AK. Curcumin inhibits tumor growth and angiogenesis in ovarian carcinoma by targeting the nuclear factor-κB pathway. *Clin Cancer Res.* 2007;13(11):3423-30.

Mehta K. Pantazis P, McQueen T, Aggarwal BB. Antiproliferative effect of Curcumin (diferuloylmethane) against human breast tumor cell lines. *Anticancer Drugs.* 1997;8(5):470-81.

Moghaddam SJ, Barta P, Mirabolfathinejad SG, Ammar-Aouchiche Z, Garza NT, Vo TI, Newman RA, Aggarwal BB, Evans CM, Tuvim MJ, Lotan R, Dickey BF. Curcumin inhibits COPD-like airway inflammation and lung cancer progression in mice. *Carcinogenesis.* 2009;30(11):1949-56.

Mukhopadhyay A, Bueso-Ramos C, Chatterjee D, Pantazis P, Aggarwal BB. Curcumin downregulates cell survival mechanisms in human prostate cancer cell lines. *Oncogene.* 2001;20(52):7597-609.

Pal A, Sung B, Bhanu Prasad BA, Schuber PT Jr, Prasad S, Aggarwal BB, Bornmann WG. Curcumin glucuronides: assessing the proliferative activity against human cell lines. *Bioorg Med Chem.* 2014;22(1):435-39.

 

Prakobwong S, Gupta SC, Kim JH, Sung B, Pinlaor P, Hiraku Y, Wongkham S, Sripa B, Pinlaor S, Aggarwal BB. Curcumin suppresses proliferation and induces apoptosis in human biliary cancer cells through modulation of multiple cell signaling pathways. *Carcinogenesis*. 2011a;32(9):1372-80.

Prakobwong S, Khoontawad J, Yongvanit P, Pairojkul C, Hiraku Y, Sithithawom P, Pinlaor P, Aggarwal BB, Pinlaor S. Curcumin decreases cholangiocarcinogenesis in hamsters by suppressing inflammation mediated molecular events related to multistep carcinogenesis. *Int J Cancer*. 2011b;129(1):88-100.

Sandur SK, Pandey MK, Sung B, Ahn KS, Murakami A, Sethi G, Limtrakul P, Badmaev V, Aggarwal BB. Curcumin, demethoxycurcumin, bisdemethoxycurcumin, tetrahydrocurcumin and turmerones differentially regulate anti-inflammatory and anti-proliferative responses through a ROS-independent mechanism. *Carcinogenesis*. 2007a;28(8):1765-73.

Sandur SK, Ichikawa H, Pandey MK, Kunnumakkara AB, Sung B, Sethi G, Aggarwal BB. Role of prooxidants and antioxidants in the anti-inflammatory and apoptotic effects of Curcumin (diferuloylmethane). *Free Radic Biol Med*. 2007b;43(4):568-80.

Sandur SK, Deorukhkar A, Pandey MK, Pabon AM, Shentu S, Guha S, Aggarwal BB, Krishnan S. Curcumin modulates the radiosensitivity of colorectal cancer cells by suppressing constitutive and inducible NF-κB activity. *Intl Radiat Oncol Biol Phys*. 2009;75(2):534-42.

Sharma C, Kaur J, Shishodia S, Aggarwal BB, Ralhan R. Curcumin down regulates smokeless tobaccoinduced NF-κB activation and COX-2 expression in human oral premalignant and cancer cells. *Toxicology*. 2006;228(1):1-15.

Shishodia S, Potdar P, Gairola CG, Aggarwal BB. Curcumin (diferuloylmethane) down-regulates cigarette smoke-induced NF-κB activation through inhibition of IκBalpha kinase in human lung epithelial cells: correlation with suppression of COX-2, MMP-9 and cyclin 01. *Carcinogenesis*. 2003;24(7):1269-79.

Shishodia S, Amin HM, Lai R, Aggarwal BB. Curcumin (diferuloylmethane) inhibits constitutive NF-κB activation, induces Gl/S arrest, suppresses proliferation, and induces apoptosis in mantle cell lymphoma. *Biochem Pharmacol*. 2005;70(5):700-13.

Singh M, Ramos I, Asafu-Adjei D, Quispe-Tintaya W, Chandra D, Jahangir A, Zang X, Aggarwal BB, Gravekamp C. Curcumin improves the therapeutic efficacy of Listeria(at)-Mage-b vaccine in correlation with improved T-cell responses in blood of a triple-negative breast cancer model 4T1. *Cancer Med*. 2013;2(4):571-82.

Singh S and Aggarwal BB. Activation of transcription factor NF-κB is suppressed by Curcumin (diferuloylmethane) [corrected]. *J Biol Chem*. 1995;270(42):24995-5000. Erratum in: *J Biol Chem*. 1995;270(50):30235.

Siwak DR, Shishodia S, Aggarwal BB, Kurzrock R Curcumin-induced antiproliferative and proapoptotic effects in melanoma cells are associated with suppression of IKB kinase and nuclear factor κB activity and are independent of the B-Raf/mitogen-activated/ extracellular signal-regulated protein kinase pathway and the Akt pathway. *Cancer*. 2005; 104(4):879-90.

Takada Y, Bhardwaj A, Potdar P, Aggarwal BB. Nonsteroidal anti-inflammatory agents differ in their ability to suppress NF -κB activation, inhibition of expression of cydooxygenase-2 and cydin D1, and abrogation of tumor cell proliferation. *Oncogene*. 2004; 23(57):9247-58.

Tharakan ST, Inamoto T, Sung B, Aggarwal BB, Kamat AM. Curcumin potentiates the antitumor effects of gemcitabine in an orthotopic model of human bladder cancer through suppression of proliferative and angiogenic biomarkers. *Biochem Pharmacol*. 2010;79(2):218-28.

Vadhan-Raj S, Weber DM, Wang M, Giralt SA, Thomas SK, Alexanian R. Zhou X, Patel P, Bueso-Ramos CE, Newman RA, Aggarwal BB. Curcumin Downregulates NF-κB and Related Genes in Patients with Multiple Myeloma: Results of a Phase I/II Study. *Blood* (ASH Annual Meeting Abstracts) 2007: Abstract 1177.

Yadav VR, Prasad S, Kannappan R, Ravindran J, Chaturvedi MM, Vaahtera L, Parkkinen J, Aggarwal BB. Cyclodextrin-complexed curcumin exhibits anti-inflammatory and antiproliferative activities superior to those of Curcumin through higher cellular uptake. *Biochem Pharmacol*. 2010;80(7):1021-32.

Zambre AP, Kulkarni VM, Padhye S, Sandur SK, Aggarwal BB. Novel Curcumin analogs targeting TNF induced NF-κB activation and proliferation in human leukemic KBM-5 cells. *Bioorg Med Cherm*. 2006;14(21):7196-204.

Zhang C, Li B, Zhang X, Hazarika P, Aggarwal BB, Duvic M. Curcumin selectively induces apoptosis in cutaneous T-celllymphoma cell lines and patients' PBMCs: potential role for STAT-3 and NF-κB signaling. *J Invest* Dermatol. 2010;130(8):2110-19.

**AP-1 (Activator Protein-1)**
A heterodimeric protein which functions as a transcription factor and regulates gene expression of cytokines, growth factors etc.

**BCG (Bacillus Calmette-Guerin)**
A vaccine for protection against tuberculosis and for treatment of some bladder cancers

**BDMC (Bisdemethoxycurcumin)**
A natural demethoxy derivative of Curcumin

**CCA (Cholangiocarcinoma)**
Type of cancer involving mutation of epithelial cells
CDC (Cyclodextrin Complex of Curcumin)

**cIAP-1 (Cellular Inhibitor of Apoptosis Protein)**
Group of proteins functioning to mediate the process of programmed cell death

**COPD (Chronic Obstructive Pulmonary Disease)**
Progressive lung disorder characterised by sputum productions, shortness of breath and cough

**CRC (Colorectal Cancer)**
Cancer formation in parts of the large intestine, typically the colon and rectum

**CS (Chitosan)**
Linear polysaccharide which is a derivative of chitin and makes up the exoskeleton of crustaceans

**CTCL (Cutaneous T-Cell Lymphoma)**
A cancer of the immune system and is a rare class of non-Hodgkin lymphoma

**CUR (Curcumin)**
The principal curcuminoid present in turmeric. Possesses anti-inflammatory, anti-diabetic, anti-cancer and anti-angiogenic properties

**DBA (Dibenzylideneacetone)**
A bright yellow coloured solid which is insoluble in water and often used as a component of sunscreens formulations

**DBM (Dibenzoylmethane)**
An aromatic 1,3-diketone derivative of acetylacetone (acac), where both methyl groups in acac have been substituted by phenyl groups

**DMC (Demethoxycurcumin)**
A natural demethoxy derivative of Curcumin

**EC (Endothelial Cells)**
Cells which form the endothelium; a layer of squamous cells lining the inner surface of blood and lymphatic vessels

**ELAM-1 (Endothelial Leukocyte Adhesion Molecule-1)**
A cell surface glycoprotein expressed by cytokine-activated endothelium

**ERK (Extracellular Signal-Regulated Protein Kinase)**
A central signalling pathway involved in the regulation of processes like proliferation, differentiation and cell cycle progression

**ERLOTINIB**
A drug used to treat non-small cell lung cancer

**GEFTINIB**
Used in the treatment of non-small cell lung cancer in patients treated with other chemotherapy medications and have not improved or whose condition has worsened

**HER2**
A member of the human epidermal growth factor receptor whose over expression is implicated in the development and progression of breast cancer

**HERCEPTIN**
Drug also known as Trastuzumab and used in the treatment of metastatic breast cancer

**HNSCC (Head And Neck Squamous Cell Carcinoma)**
A malignant tumour of the head and neck region

**HUMIRA®**
Also known as adalimumab, used in the treatment of rheumatoid arthritis, juvenile idiopathic arthritis, psoriatic arthritis, ankylosing spondylitis, and plaque psoriasis

**ICAM-1 (Intracellular Adhesion Molecule-1)**
These proteins are part of the immunoglobulin superfamily and mediate processes like inflammation, immune responses and various other intracellular signalling events

**IKK (Iκb-alpha Kinase)**
A protein which masks the signal of NF-κB transcription factor and maintains it in an inactive form

**IL-6 (Interleukin-6)**
Cytokine involved in inflammatory responses and in the regulation of metabolic, regenerative and neural functioning

**MCL (Human Mantle Cell Lymphoma)**
A rare non-Hodgkin lymphoma mostly affecting men over the age of 60

**MDR (Multidrug-Resistant)**
A condition permitting microorganisms to evade the effects of various antimicrobials especially antibiotics

**MDSC (Myeloid-Derived Suppressor Cells)**
A heterogeneous cell population that proliferates during cancer, inflammation and infection

**MEK (Mitogen-Activated Signal-Regulated Protein Kinase)**
A signalling cascade responsible for transmitting signals from the cell surface receptor to the cell nucleus

**mTOR (Mammalian Target of Rapamycin)**
An evolutionarily conserved serine-threonine kinase that is known to sense the environmental and cellular nutrition and energy status

**NNK (Nicotine-derived nitrosamine ketone)**
A nitrosamine present in tobacco which has been implicated in carcinogenesis

**NSAIDS (Non-steroidal Anti-Inflammatory Drugs)**
Medication with analgesic and antipyretic effects

**NTHI (Non-Typeable Hemophilus Influenzae)**
Gram negative bacteria that are opportunistic pathogens and are responsible for causing diseases like bacteremia, pneumonia, epiglottitis and acute bacterial meningitis

**PARP (Poly(Adp)Ribose Polymerase)**
Group of proteins supporting processes involving DNA repair and apoptosis

**PEG (Polyethylene Glycol)**
A polyether compound with many applications from industrial manufacturing to medicine

**PLGA (Poly(lactic-co-glycolic acid))**
A polymer which has various medical applications like use in sutures

**RANKL (Receptor Activator of NF-κB Ligand)**
A member of the tumour necrosis family also known as a type II membrane protein. Plays a role in the immune system functioning and bone regeneration and remodeling.

**REMICADE®**
Drug used in the treatment of rheumatoid arthritis, psoriatic arthritis, ulcerative colitis and Crohn's disease

**ROS (Reactive Oxygen Species)**
Chemically reactive molecules containing oxygen that are formed as part of normal metabolism. They play a vital role in homeostasis and cell signalling.

**SF (Silk Fibroin)**
An insoluble protein present in silk created by spiders and also used in tissue regeneration procedures

**STAT3 (Signal Transducer and Activator of Transcription 3)**
Group of proteins/transcription factors that are activated in response to cytokines and growth factors

**TAA (Tumor-Associated Antigens)**
Can derive from any protein or glycoprotein synthesized by the tumor cell

**THC (Tetrahydrocurcumin)**
An antioxidative substance which is derived from Curcumin

**TME (Tumor Microenvironment)**
The term indicates the cellular environment of the tumour and includes immune cells, signalling molecules, lymphocytes, bone marrow-derived inflammatory cells etc.

**TNBC (Triple-Negative Breast Cancer)**
Form of breast cancer which doesn't express the estrogen receptor, progesterone receptor or Her2/neu genes

**TNF-α (Tumor Necrosis Factor-α)**
pro-inflammatory cytokine also involved in the stimulation of apoptosis

**TRAIL (Tumor Necrosis Factor-Related Apoptosis-Inducing Ligand)**
A cytokine produces by normal tissue and implicated in stimulation of processes like apoptosis

**VCAM-1 (Vascular Cell Adhesion Molecule-1)**
Involved in cell to cell adhesion processes and are regulators of atherosclerosis, cancer cell metastasis and inflammation

# *Curcumin C3 Complex®*

## *The Most Clinically Studied Curcumin Brand in the World*

Nature's Own Pharma Cocrystal...

**Muhammed Majeed, Ph.D.**

&

his Scientific Team

# Setting The Gold Standard *for Curcuminoids*

- ✓ Introduction
- ✓ Genesis of Curcumin C3 Complex®

# Introduction

Rising incidence of lifestyle and age-related diseases, side effects of drugs in western medication system and heavy cost for managing these health conditions have turned people more towards natural healthcare system. Today, we are experiencing what can be termed as a herbal renaissance, which has increased the use of natural or nature-based supplements and drugs for the management of chronic ailments. Researchers acknowledge the utility of traditional herbs and their way of healing, which exists from time immemorial. Turmeric is one of the most popular traditionally used herb and also known as " **the golden spice**". It is grown in various parts of India and other Asian countries, and has been held sacred since ancient times. Curcumin is the major and the active ingredient of turmeric (*Curcuma longa*), and also responsible for its yellow color. Turmeric has strong relation with the socio-cultural life of the Indian subcontinent and in Vedic period people regarded it as "herb of the sun" [Duggi *et al.* 2013].

In Ayurveda, the traditional Indian system of medicine, the therapeutic role of turmeric has been described as Dashemani Lekhaniya (emaciating), Kusthagna (anti-dermatosis) and Visaghna (anti-poisonous) [Krup *et al.* 2013]. Since ancient time, turmeric has been used as a traditional medicine in the treatment of various diseases like asthma, cough, allergic rhinitis, urinary disorders, jaundice, diarrhea, biliary disorders, anorexia, diabetic wounds, sprains and swellings caused by injury. The dried turmeric powder has been used topically for insect stings, chickenpox and smallpox [Ravindran *et al.* 2007].

In the modern scientific world, Curcumin has been the subject of extensive study into its mechanism of action and therapeutic use in managing several diseases. It has been described to possess antioxidant, anti-inflammatory, antibacterial, antifungal, antiparasitic, antimutagenic, anticancer and detox properties [Majeed *et al.* 1999]. Since the antioxidant activities of Curcumin are not degraded by heat (unlike most vitamins), even using the spice in cooking provide benefits. In other words it is also "the spice of life."

# *Genesis of Curcumin C3 Complex®*

While Curcumin caught the attention of researchers when it was first isolated, the path to make it a successful dietary supplement had long ways to go. Ayurveda practiced in India for ages used turmeric in several traditional formulations and was provided as personalized treatment by practitioners. However, there was no concept of standardization and there were no efforts to carry out pharmacokinetic or pharmacodynamic studies of these formulations, which was a major hurdle while using these formulations in the Western world. Standardization of herbal formulations is essential in order to assess the quality of medicines based on the concentration of actives [Nhawkar *et al.* 2014]. This was realized by the researchers at Sami/Sabinsa in the very early days of their work on turmeric. Sabinsa, for the first time introduced the concept of standardization of actives in turmeric extracts to ensure that by applying modern science we can bring the best out of Ayurveda. This concept of bio-standardization was later used in several herbal products by the industry as a standard tool. Team of scientists at Sabinsa Corporation, while working on this traditional herb, derived an optimized composition of Curcuminoids from rhizomes of turmeric to provide maximum antioxidant and bioprotectant activity. This composition was later patented by Sabinsa Corporation. This unique and patented composition of Curcuminoids is available as a dietary supplement/nutraceutical/functional food/health food under the brand name of "**Curcumin C3 Complex®**." Curcumin C3 Complex® achieved a major landmark in 2013 when it received a "**No Comment Letter**" from the USFDA, which meant that Sabinsa's Curcumin C3 Complex® achieved the **Generally Recognized as Safe (GRAS)** status and now could be used in the food category as well. The "Bioprotectant" action of Curcuminoids in Curcumin C3 Complex® provides optimal antioxidant protection and maintains integrity of the biological system. The major components of Curcumin C3 Complex® are Curcumin, Demethoxycurcumin and Bis-demethoxycurcumin (Fig. 1). In Curcumin C3 Complex®, Curcumin makes up 75-81% of total Curcuminoids, Demethoxycurcumin about 15-19% and

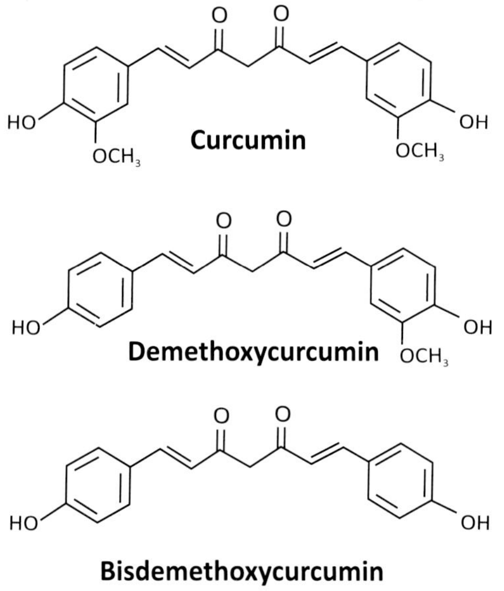


**Fig. 1:** Structure of Curcumin, Demethoxycurcumin (DMC) and Bisdemethoxycurcumin (BDMC)

Bisdemethoxycurcumin about 2.2-6.5% [Majeed *et al.* 1999]. Curcumin exists in both keto and enol forms, Fig.1 represents keto form of Curcumin, Demethoxycurcumin and Bisdemethoxycurcumin.

Today, Sabinsa's Curcumin C3 Complex® enjoys the special status of being the "**most extensively studied and clinically documented**" Curcuminoids brand available in the world. There are more than 80 research papers including 45 clinical studies published in peer-reviewed journals to date (September 2015). These large numbers of clinical trials address the pharmacokinetics, safety and efficacy of this nutraceutical for numerous diseases and health conditions in humans (Fig. 2). The journey of Sabinsa's clinical trials has helped exploring the potential of Curcumin in preventive healthcare and has carved a unique place for Curcumin in the dietary supplement industry making Curcumin C3 Complex® "**The Most Trusted Brand**" for over two decades.

Majority of the studies have evaluated Curcumin for its anti-inflammatory and antioxidant activities. Its anti-inflammatory activity is associated with its ability to inhibit NF-κB, TNF-α, COX-2, Lipoxygenase (LOX) and inducible nitric oxide synthase. Upregulation of COX-2 and/or inducible nitric oxide synthase has been associated with the pathology of human cancer and various disorders. Curcumin's ability to regulate carcinogen-detoxifying enzymes such as glutathione-S-transferase (GST) and suppression of isoenzyme COX-2 has made it a potent chemopreventive and chemotherapeutic agent.

 

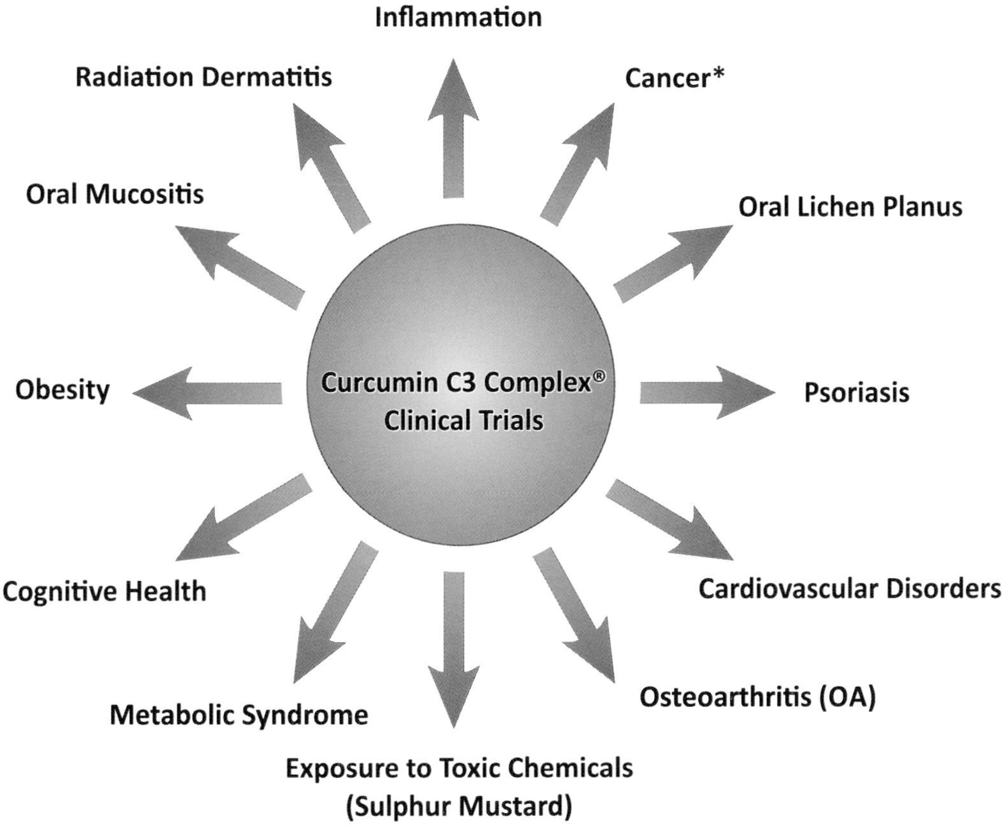


* Pancreatic Cancer, Multiple Myeloma, Monoclonal Gammopathy of Undefined Significance, Colorectal Cancer, Breast Cancer, Non-Hodgkin's Lymphoma, Smoldering Multiple Myeloma

**Fig. 2:** Curcumin and its potential health benefits

# Curcumin C3 Complex®
## *in Completed Clinical Trials*

- ✓ Safety and Dose-escalation Studies
- ✓ Cancer
- ✓ Radiation Dermatitis
- ✓ Inflammation
- ✓ Cognitive Health
- ✓ Obesity
- ✓ Metabolic Syndrome
- ✓ Cardiovascular Disorders
- ✓ Bioavailability
- ✓ Oxidative Stress - A Meta-analysis
- ✓ C-Reactive Protein Lowering Effect - A Meta-analysis

# Safety and Dose-escalation Studies

Botanicals and supplements of natural origin for general health and wellness are widely used but skeptically viewed at the same time. The issue of safety is critically important since many products in the market do not provide sufficient data on the same. Curcumin, although extensively used traditionally has also been clinically evaluated for its safety in the following studies. Attempts have also been made to maximize the dosage to study the maximum tolerable dosage.

In this section, we detail papers where Curcumin C3 Complex® has been evaluated for its safety in healthy human subjects and individuals with advanced cancer.

Phase I Clinical Trial of Oral Curcumin: Biomarkers of Systemic Activity and Compliance

# Phase I clinical trial of oral curcumin: biomarkers of systemic activity and compliance

Sharma *et al.*

*Clin Cancer Res.* 2004

Researchers at University of Leicester and University of Liverpool, UK conducted a clinical trial focusing on safety of high dosage of Curcumin in patients with advanced cancer and exploring the sensitive biomarkers for efficacy of Curcumin supplementation. Fifteen subjects with histologically proven adenocarcinoma of colon or rectum were enrolled. Curcumin C3 Complex® capsules of 500 mg (containing 450 mg of Curcumin, 40 mg of demethoxycurcumin and 10 mg bisdemethoxycurcumin) each were provided to the subjects at dosage of 450 mg, 900 mg, 1800 mg or 3600 mg of Curcuminoids once daily in their respective dose levels for 4 months. Results showed that at a dosage of 3.6 g daily, the levels of prostaglandin E2 (PGE2) when compared for pre-dose, post-dose levels were found significantly lower (Fig. 3). Different metabolites of Curcumin were also measured in those patients (Fig. 4)

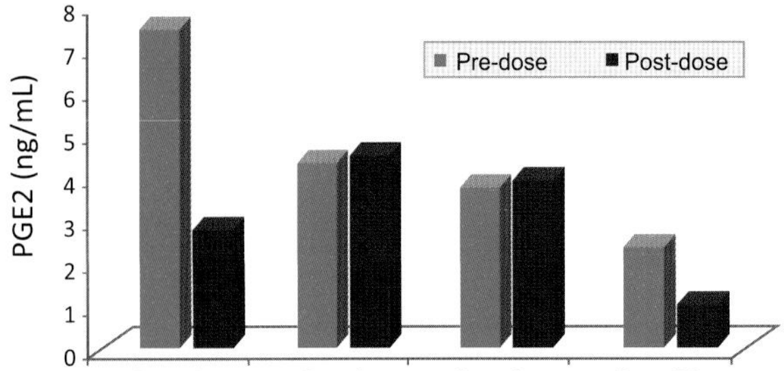


**Fig. 3:** LPS-induced PGE2 levels in plasma of patients who received 3.6 g Curcumin daily

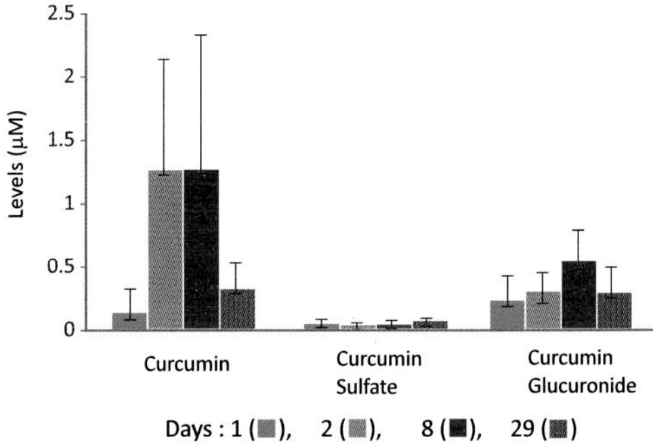


**Fig. 4:** Levels of Curcumin, Curcumin sulfate and glucuronide in urine

Curcumin is well known to inhibit COX-2 enzyme, which is responsible for PGE2 synthesis. COX-2 enzyme is also thought to play a pathogenic role in carcinogenesis of many tissues; its pharmacological modulation holds implications for cancer prevention. Based on these positive findings, authors of this study suggested the use of measurement of PGE2 as a biomarker in target tissues to understand the systemic anticancer activity of Curcuminoids. The analysis of urine samples suggested the presence of Curcumin and its conjugates in all subjects consuming the 3.6 g of Curcumin C3 Complex® [Sharma *et al.* 2004].

BMC Complementary and Alternative Medicine

Research article

Dose escalation of a curcuminoid formulation

Christopher D Lao[1], Mack T Ruffin IV*[2], Daniel Normolle[3], Dennis D Heath[4], Sandra I Murray[1], Joanne M Bailey[2], Martha E Boggs[1], James Crowell[5], Cheryl L Rock[6] and Dean E Brenner[1]

## Dose-escalation of a curcuminoid formulation

Lao *et al.*

*BMC Complement Altern Med.* 2006

For a chemopreventive intervention to be successful, it must be provided in dosages that are effective and free from any dose-related toxicity. Keeping in mind the safety of Curcumin supplementation, a Phase I study was performed in healthy human volunteers to determine the maximum tolerable dosage. This clinical trial was published jointly by researchers from University of Michigan, University of California and National Cancer Institute Bethesda, Maryland, USA [Lao *et al.* 2006].

Twenty-four subjects (13 men and 11 women) were recruited in this clinical trial who had not consumed turmeric in previous 14 days. Subjects were administered consecutively at dose levels from 5-12 g. The safety was assessed for 72 h following the Curcumin dose and different Curcumin metabolites were measured in the urine. The study results showed that there was only minimal toxicity up to 12 g single dosage of Curcumin C3 Complex®.

Researchers concluded that Curcumin C3 Complex® at a dose up to 12 g showed excellent tolerance in humans. This was the first "**maximum tolerable dose**" study conducted on any brand of Curcumin and is often cited in the nutritional industry for Curcumin safety.

The results from above two clinical studies showed that Curcumin C3 Complex® was well tolerated at high dosage up to 12 g. Phase I clinical study on colon cancer patients also proved its safety and efficacy of high dosages (3.6 g) for long term use as well. These dose-related tolerability studies encouraged future clinical studies on various types of cancer, since the tolerability and toxicity of a nutritional supplement is an important parameter while exploring possibility of its application as an anticancer adjuvant.

# Cancer

In recent times, Curcumin has gained its popularity through several studies which were performed on various cancer cell lines and human clinical trials done on subjects suffering from cancer. To understand the role of Curcumin in cancer, we should understand cancer as well.

Cancer is a condition in which certain abnormal cells divide without control and spread to invade different parts and organs of the body. Based on the affected organ, cancer can be of more than 100 types, but broadly it can be divided in to 4 groups:

- **Carcinoma**: This type of cancer arises from the cell layers that cover the surface of body or organs such as skin and colon (arising from colon cells). Majority of the cancers belong to this group
- **Sarcoma**: This type of cancer arises from connective tissues such as muscles, cartilage, bone and fibrous connective tissue
- **Leukemia**: Leukemia arises from blood forming tissues such as bone marrow
- **Lymphoma**: It originates from the immune system cells

Human body consists of 10-13 trillion cells, which have definite life span and almost all of the cells get turned over within a span of 3-4 months. Hence, cell death is a very natural phenomenon in a living human being. In contrast to normal cells, cancer cells evade cell death and in fact start showing limitless replication capability, spread in the body through angiogenesis and invade different tissues.

Hence, agents which can trigger cell death or apoptosis (programmed cell death) can be potential anticancer compounds.

 

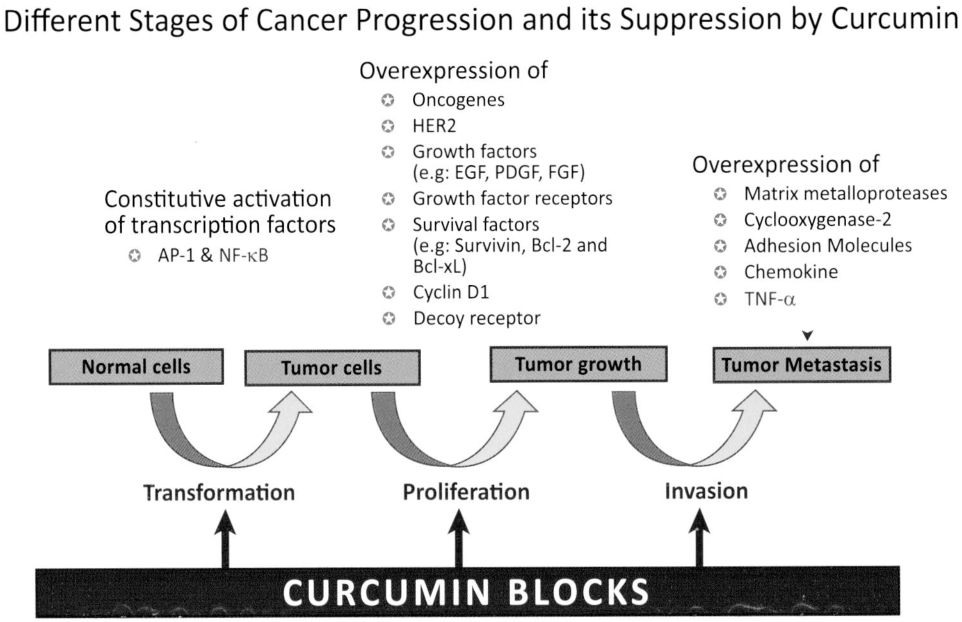


**Fig. 5:** Curcumin and its potential pathways involved in anticancer activity (Courtesy: Aggarwal *et al*. 2003)

Curcumin is unique as it inhibits cancer initiation, proliferation as well as metastasis. It directly or indirectly modulates various molecular targets including transcription factors, growth factors, receptors, cytokines, genes responsible for cell proliferation and apoptosis. Due to its effect on diverse range of molecular targets, it can inhibit the proliferation of almost all types of cancer cells by activating the growth inhibitory pathway in cancer cells. Curcuminoids can affect the growth of cancer cells by regulation of multiple cell signaling pathways including cell proliferation pathway (cyclin D1), cell survival pathway (Bcl-2, Bcl-xL, cFLIP), tumor suppressor pathway (p35, p21) and protein kinase pathways (c-Jun N-terminal kinase, Akt and AMP-activated protein kinase) (Fig. 5).

Curcumin has a differential action on cancer cells and normal cells. In other words, Curcumin kills the tumor cells and yet does no harm to normal cells. Though it is not a very well understood mechanism, one hypothesis here is that Curcumin has higher cellular uptake in tumor cells than in normal cells. It could also be affected by lower glutathione levels in tumor cells, which causes more uptake or higher sensitivity towards Curcumin in cancer cells.

Thus, due to its diverse mechanisms of action, Curcumin may be helpful against wide variety of cancer cells and this has been the focus of several studies conducted *in vitro* and clinical on various cancer types [Ravindran *et al.* 2009]. In the following sections, we will be discussing trials conducted on patients suffering from various types of cancer.

# Pancreatic Cancer

Pancreatic cancer is one of the most lethal types of cancer with poor survival prognosis. Curcumin's anticancer activity is related to its inhibitory action on the NF-κB transcription factor and genes regulated by NF-κB such as Bcl-2, Bcl-xL, cyclin D1, c-myc, vascular endothelial growth factor, matrix metallopeptidase and so on. These factors are involved in anti-apoptosis, proliferation, angiogenesis and invasion of cancer, which is of much interest to the researchers looking for antitumor molecules. In earlier preclinical studies, Curcumin has been shown to suppress NF-κB activation, which makes it an interesting agent to study its effect in patients with pancreatic cancer.

The standard chemotherapy for pancreatic cancer includes antimetabolite gemcitabine, which has improved rate of clinical benefit response (CBR) and survival over 5-fluorouracil. In *in vitro* and *in vivo* studies it was observed that Curcumin could sensitize pancreatic cancer to gemcitabine.

Curcumin and Gemcitabine in Patients With Advanced Pancreatic Cancer

Ron Epelbaum
Rambam Health Care Campus, Haifa, Israel, and Technion-Israel Institute of Technology, Haifa, Israel

Moshe Schaffer and Bella Vizel
Rambam Health Care Campus, Haifa, Israel

Vladimir Badmaev
Sabinsa Corporation, Piscataway, New Jersey, USA

Gil Bar-Sela
Rambam Health Care Campus, Haifa, Israel, and Technion-Israel Institute of Technology, Haifa, Israel

# Curcumin and gemcitabine in patients with advanced Pancreatic Cancer

Epelbaum *et al.*

*Nutr Cancer*. 2010

Based on the preliminary data, researchers at Technion-Israel Institute of Technology, Haifa, Israel conducted an open-labeled, phase II clinical trial using Curcumin as an adjuvant to gemcitabine therapy. Seventeen patients with advanced or metastatic adenocarcinoma were enrolled for the trial. The objective of the study was to evaluate the activity and feasibility of gemcitabine-Curcumin combination. Subjects received 8 g of Curcumin orally along with 1.0 $g/m^2$ of gemcitabine intravenously for 3 of the 4 weeks in the clinical trial. Curcumin was administered orally in divided dosage of 4000 mg twice daily on empty stomach. Though, due to small sample size this study did not show conclusive results regarding the efficacy of Curcumin, however, it paved way for future trials with Curcumin as potential adjuvant to gemcitabine. Authors of the above study also suggested the use of adjuvant like piperine with Curcumin for increasing the bioavailability of Curcumin [Epelbaum *et al.* 2010].

ORIGINAL ARTICLE

A phase I/II study of gemcitabine-based chemotherapy plus curcumin for patients with gemcitabine-resistant pancreatic cancer

## A phase I/II study of gemcitabine-based chemotherapy plus Curcumin for patients with gemcitabine-resistant Pancreatic Cancer

Kanai *et al.*

*Cancer Chemother Pharmacol.* 2011

Following the above trial, a phase I/II clinical trial was conducted at two Japanese institutions (Kyoto University Hospital and Kitano Hospital, Osaka) for determining the safety and feasibility of oral Curcumin in combination with gemcitabine-based chemotherapy. Twenty-one patients suffering from advanced pancreatic cancer and exhibiting gemcitabine resistance (patients showed progression of disease during gemcitabine-based chemotherapy) were enrolled. The clinical study was conducted in 2 phases. In the Phase I study, the dose-related safety of oral Curcumin at 8 g dosage with gemcitabine-based chemotherapy was evaluated. Since the subjects completed the first treatment cycle without any dose-limiting toxicity (DLT), 8 g/day dosage was chosen for Phase II trial. In the Phase II clinical study, 100% patient compliance was recorded despite the poor condition of the patients after failure of gemcitabine monotherapy. Phase II results also showed improvement in chemotherapy-related symptoms on supplementation with Curcumin C3 Complex®. Survival rate of pancreatic cancer patients after failure of first line of gemcitabine therapy was very poor, however, the results from this clinical study were very encouraging with median overall survival time of 161 days and one-year survival rate of 19% observed in pancreatic cancer patients. Researchers of the study were able to conclude that Curcumin supplementation can be considered adjuvant to gemcitabine-based chemotherapy without increasing any clinically relevant toxicity. Researchers did not find any cumulative toxicity of combination of gemcitabine and Curcumin C3 Complex® and hence, this combination was found to be safe and well tolerated [Kanai *et al.* 2011].

While the above two studies showed safety of using Curcumin as an adjuvant to gemcitabine therapy, another clinical study conducted at MD Anderson Cancer Center, USA evaluated the safety and efficacy of Curcumin as a standalone supplement in patients with advanced pancreatic cancer who could not receive any radiotherapy or chemotherapy.

Cancer Therapy: Clinical

Phase II Trial of Curcumin in Patients with Advanced Pancreatic Cancer

## Phase II trial of Curcumin in patients with advanced pancreatic cancer

Dhillon *et al.*

*Clin Cancer Res.* 2008

In this non-randomized, open-label, Phase II trial, 25 subjects with advanced pancreatic cancer who could not receive any radio or chemotherapy were enrolled. Starting dose based on the prior studies was suggested at 8 g/day orally until the disease progressed. Since NF-κB is constitutively involved in pancreatic cancer progression, the results for cytokine levels in the subjects who received Curcumin supplementation were observed with interest. Results showed that majority of patients exhibited downregulation of NF-κB and COX-2 after treatment with Curcumin, though this decrease could not reach significant levels. No toxic effects related to Curcumin supplementation were observed during the study. This was the first study to show that Curcumin can downregulate the expression of these molecules in humans. In one of the subjects, there was 73% reduction in the tumor size by response evaluation criteria in solid tumors (Fig. 6).

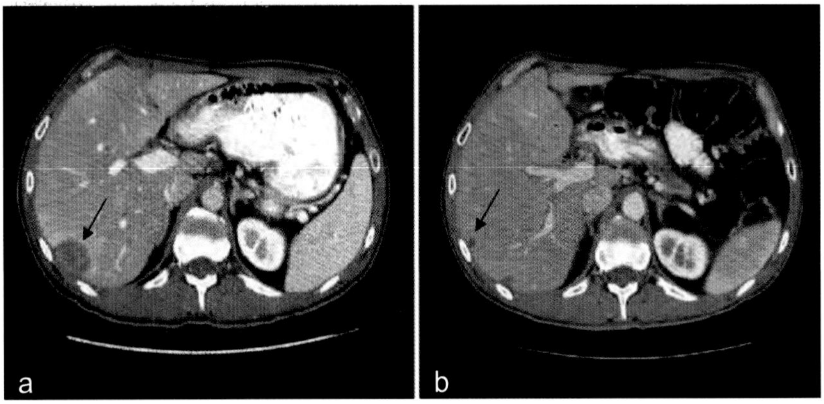


**Fig. 6:** Computed tomography scan (CT) of abdomen (a) pretherapy (b) post-therapy showing hepatic lesions in patient no. 8. The lesion showed 73% decrease in size by response evaluation criteria in solid tumors

Curcumin supplementation also showed decrease in pSTAT3 activation in most patients. Signal transducers and activators of transcription (STATs) play an important role in cell differentiation and inflammation and its activation is observed in tumor cells. By downregulating the pSTAT3, Curcumin exhibits its activity against tumorigenesis and chemoresistance. This clinical trial showed safety and biological activity in patients with pancreatic cancer [Dhillon *et al.* 2008].

# Multiple Myeloma

Multiple myeloma is a cancer that forms in plasma cells, a type of white blood cell, which is responsible for making antibodies that can recognize foreign proteins or antigens from invasive micro-organisms and help in fighting infections. These plasma cells reside in the bone marrow in the hollow bones. When the plasma cells become cancerous, they can produce tumors also known as plasmacytoma. However, when plasmacytoma migrates to soft tissues such as throat tonsils or paranasal sinuses it can cause a condition known as multiple myeloma. As the number of myeloma cells increase, the production of RBCs, WBCs and platelets decrease drastically.

The treatment choice for multiple myeloma patients is limited to radiotherapy, surgery or chemotherapy with immunomodulatory drugs such as Thalidomide and Lenalidomide. On the other hand, Curcumin, due to its activity against diverse pathways affecting both haemotological and non-haematological cancer is a potential candidate for use in multiple myeloma, which sensitizes these cells towards the immunomodulatory drugs.

In the below section, we will discuss some of the studies where Curcumin C3 Complex® was used in subjects with multiple myeloma.

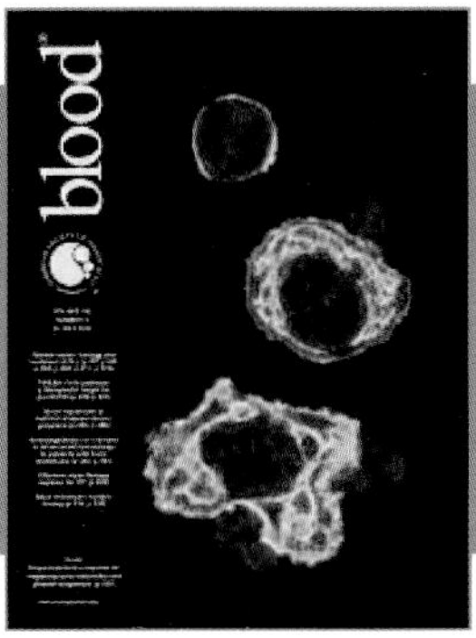


## Curcumin downregulates NF-κB and related genes in patients with Multiple myeloma: Results of a phase I/II study

Vadhan-Raj *et al.*

*Blood* 2007

This clinical study was conducted by researchers at MD Anderson Cancer Center, USA, where a great deal of work has been carried out on Curcumin's anticancerous activity both *in vitro* and *in vivo*. This study was conducted to evaluate the safety and efficacy of Curcuminoids in patients with multiple myeloma. Curcumin has been shown to potently suppress the activation of these transcription factors in cultured cells. In this 12-week study, 29 patients were recruited and were administered a daily dose of Curcumin C3 Complex® at 2, 4, 6, 8 or 12 g/day in combination with BioPerine® at 10 mg in 2 divided doses. Expression of surrogate biomarkers such as NF-κB, COX-2 and pSTAT3 from blood were studied for evaluating the effect of treatment. Results showed that treatment with Curcumin and BioPerine® was well tolerated with no significant adverse events. Out of 29 recruited patients, 12 patients continued the treatment (more than 12 weeks) and five patients were treated with different doses (one patient: 4 g, two patients: 6 g and two patients: 8 g) and completed a year of treatment with stable disease. In this study the total Curcumin levels with conjugated form were dependent on both doses and duration of administration. Results from this study indicated that oral administration of Curcumin significantly downregulated the levels of NF-κB ($p<0.0001$), STAT3 ($p<0.001$) and suppressed COX-2 ($p<0.0001$). This is the first report to indicate that Curcumin, a highly safe agent, is bioavailable and can downregulate NF-κB, STAT3 and COX-2 in multiple myeloma patients. Therefore, there is a need to investigate a potential therapeutic role of Curcumin either alone or as a modulator of chemo-resistance in combination with other active agents. The researchers acknowledged the role of BioPerine® in making Curcuminoids more bioavailable [Vadhan-Raj *et al.* 2007].

# *Monoclonal Gammopathy of Undefined Significance*

While multiple myeloma is a progressive disease, characterized with high bone turnover, low blood count, poor resistance, high morbidity and mortality; monoclonal gammopathy of undetermined significance (MGUS) is an asymptomatic plasma cell disorder, which can progress into multiple myeloma. Therefore, monoclonal gammopathy of undetermined significance state is considered as suitable for developing early intervention strategies to lower the risk of multiple myeloma. It is considered as a potentially fatal condition with no clear indication of the course of the disease, as it may not lead to symptomatic multiple myeloma for long time. Currently paraprotein levels in monoclonal gammopathy of undetermined significance patients are evaluated to identify the high risk patients. Another term frequently encountered is smoldering myeloma, which is an intermediate stage between monoclonal gammopathy of undetermined significance and multiple myeloma. While in monoclonal gammopathy of undetermined significance there may be only a benign clone of plasma cells in bone marrow, in smoldering myeloma there is more than 10% plasma cells affected.

Studies have shown that Curcumin exerts antiproliferative effect on tumor cells including multiple myeloma cells by downregulating interleukin-6. Hence, Curcumin can be a potential natural compound to study for the treatment of the monoclonal gammopathy of undetermined significance and its progression into multiple myeloma.

## The Potential Role of Curcumin in Patients with Monoclonal Gammopathy of Undefined Significance- Its Effect on Paraproteinemia and the Urinary N-telopeptide of Type I Collagen Bone Turnover Marker

Golombick *et al.*

*Clin Cancer Res.* 2009

Based on the above knowledge a randomized, single-blind, cross-over clinical study to evaluate the effect of Curcuminoids on patients with monoclonal gammopathy of undetermined significance patients was carried out by researchers at University of Wollongong, NSW, Australia. In this study, 26 subjects with monoclonal gammopathy of undetermined significance aged 45 years and above were enrolled at St. George Hospital, Sydney, Australia. The subjects were randomized into two groups, which were crossed over at the end of 3 months. The active group was administered 4 g Curcumin C3 Complex® orally and matching placebo to the other group. Clinical evaluation of blood and urine samples was performed at various times (baseline, 1st week, 1st month, 3rd month) during the clinical study. Researchers observed that Curcumin supplementation led to decrease in the paraprotein levels of the subjects (Fig. 7).

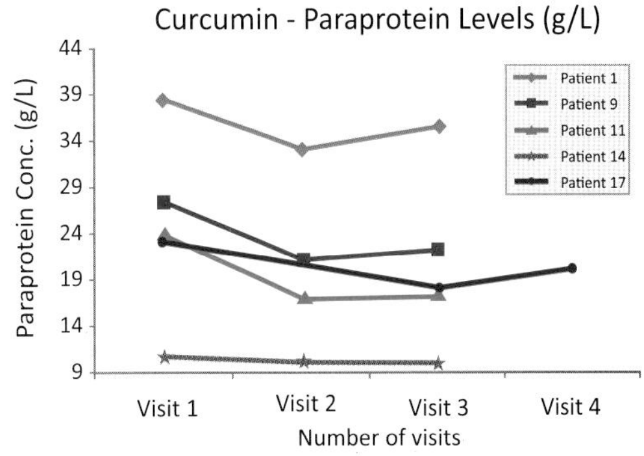


**Fig. 7:** Paraprotein levels in patients No. 1, 9, 11, 14 and 17

Twenty-seven percent of subjects showed decrease in the urinary N-telopeptide (uNTx) levels. Levels of uNTx are related to bone resorption and its reduction along with paraprotein levels is clearly indicated in response to Curcumin supplementation [Golombick *et al.* 2009].

With positive response from the above clinical study, another trial was planned with patients diagnosed with monoclonal gammopathy of undetermined significance including patients with smoldering multiple myeloma.

Research Article

Monoclonal gammopathy of undetermined significance, smoldering multiple myeloma, and curcumin: A randomized, double-blind placebo-controlled cross-over 4g study and an open-label 8g extension study

Terry Golombick,[1*] Terrence H. Diamond,[1] Arumugam Manoharan,[2] and Rajeev Ramakrishna[2]

## Monoclonal gammopathy of undetermined significance, smoldering multiple myeloma, and curcumin: a randomized, double blind placebo controlled cross over 4g study and an open label 8g extension study

Golombick *et al.*

*Am J Hematol.* 2012

A randomized, double-blind, placebo-controlled, cross-over study with 4 g dose of Curcumin C3 Complex®, followed by an open-label extension study using 8 g dose of Curcumin C3 Complex® was conducted at St. George's Hospital, Sydney, Australia. Thirty-six patients were randomized to receive either 4 g Curcumin or matching placebo, crossing over at 3 months. All subjects had an option of entering into an open-label 8 g extension study for further 3 months duration. This was the first study to describe the beneficial effects of Curcumin on free light chains (FLCs) in monoclonal gammopathy of undetermined significance and smoldering multiple myeloma patients. Free light chain refers to the immunoglobulin light chains, which are produced excessively in multiple myeloma patients and are linked to plasma cell growth in multiple myeloma. The results of this study showed that Curcumin supplementation resulted in decrease in free light chain ratio (rFLC). This reduction was found to be more in patients having abnormal rFLC at the baseline. Increase in dosage of Curcumin up to 8 g/day showed increased benefits. In view of earlier published studies that patients with an increased rFLC have increased risk of progression of monoclonal gammopathy of undetermined significance and smoldering multiple myeloma to multiple myeloma. Findings of this study suggested that Curcumin has the potential to slow the disease progression. Results of this study showed a decrease in rFLC and can be used to plan intervention strategies in patients with monoclonal gammopathy of undetermined significance and smoldering multiple myeloma to multiple myeloma [Golombick *et al.* 2012].

 

# Colorectal Cancer

Colorectal cancer is the third leading cause of cancer-related deaths in the US and the most common type of cancer when men and women are considered separately, and the second leading cause when both sexes are combined. The American Cancer Society's estimates for the number of colorectal cancer cases in the US for 2015 are 132,700. It is expected to cause about 49,700 deaths during 2015. Progression of colorectal cancer like many other types of cancer is associated with activation of multiple signaling pathways and inhibition of these signaling pathways using Curcumin C3 Complex® becomes a very natural choice. It is also well known that expression of COX-2 mRNA and protein is increased in human colorectal adenomas as compared to normal colorectal tissue, therefore anti-inflammatory role, which Curcumin C3 Complex® can play in colon tissue is of great interest. However, despite the fact that Curcumin can be a potential chemopreventive agent for colorectal cancer, it was important to examine whether Curcumin can actually reach to the therapeutic levels in the colon tissue to elicit any biochemical activity. In this section we look into some of the clinical studies conducted using Curcumin C3 Complex®, which have not only answered some of the questions on the role of Curcumin in colorectal cancer but also paved way for possibility of using Curcuminoids in strategies for managing colorectal health.

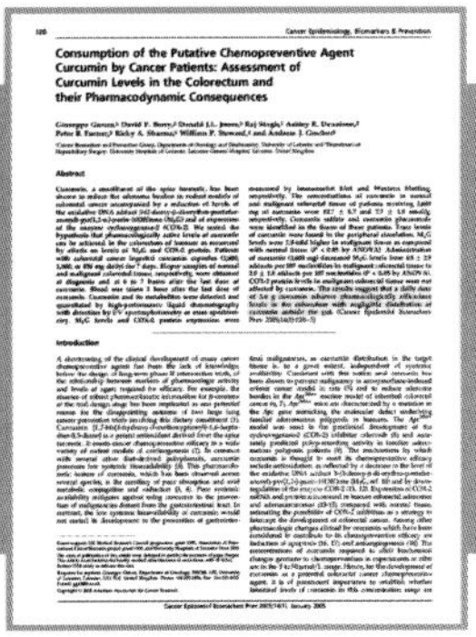
Consumption of the Putative Chemopreventive Agent Curcumin by Cancer Patients: Assessment of Curcumin Levels in the Colorectum and their Pharmacodynamic Consequences

## Consumption of putative chemopreventive agent curcumin by cancer patients: assessment of curcumin levels in the colorectum and their pharmacodynamic consequences

Garcea *et al.*

*Cancer Epidemiol Biomarkers Prev.* 2005

Researchers at University of Leicester, UK conducted a clinical trial with Curcumin as a supplement to establish whether intestinal levels of Curcumin in the concentration range required to bring chemopreventive benefits are achievable in humans. Twelve subjects with confirmed colorectal carcinoma and scheduled to go for colectomy were recruited in the clinical trial and were administered oral Curcumin at the dosage of 450, 1800 or 3600 mg per day for one week before colectomy. Results obtained from the observation of colon tissue collected from surgical procedure showed that administration of Curcumin lowered the $M_1G$ levels in the malignant tissue (Fig. 8).

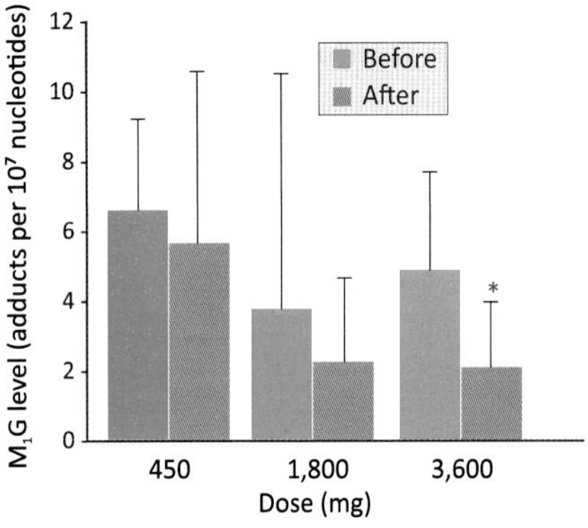


**Fig. 8:** $M_1G$ adduct levels in the malignant colorectal tissue obtained from patients before and after administration of Curcumin at dosage indicated ($p<0.05$)

$M_1G$ levels are markers for exhibiting COX-2 activity. In human colon cells, COX-2 activity is associated with formation of endogenous mutagen malondialdehyde (MDA, a biomarker for oxidative stress) and when MDA reacts with DNA it forms adduct $M_1G$. Thus, levels of $M_1G$ correlate to COX-2 expression in the tissue. Results also reviewed that regular intake of 3600 mg of Curcumin dosage can furnish drug levels in the GI tract, which can produce pharmacodynamic changes needed for chemopreventive action of Curcumin in the intestine. This study paved way for future trial for longer duration to understand the role of Curcumin in reducing COX-2 expression and long term benefits from antioxidative changes in the tissue [Garcea *et al.* 2005].

Europe PMC Funders Group
Author Manuscript
Cancer Prev Res (Phila). Author manuscript; available in PMC 2013 August 01.

**Prolonged biologically active colonic tissue levels of curcumin achieved after oral administration - a clinical pilot study including assessment of patient acceptability**

[1]Department of Cancer Studies and Molecular Medicine, University of Leicester, Leicester, UK
[2]Department of Surgery and Cancer, Imperial College, London, UK
[3]Department of Surgery, St Mark's Hospital, Harrow, UK
[4]Department of Surgery, University Hospitals of Wales, Cardiff, UK
[5]Department of Surgery, University Hospitals of Leicester, Leicester, UK

**Abstract**

# Prolonged biologically active colonic tissue levels of curcumin achieved after oral administration--a clinical pilot study including assessment of patient acceptability

Irving *et al.*

*Cancer Prev Res.* 2013

Researchers at Leicester University, UK who conducted the previous trial [Garcea *et al.* 2005] on Curcumin and its possible role in colon cancer, carried out another clinical trial to evaluate the long term use of Curcumin as part of colorectal cancer prevention strategy and to quantify the levels of Curcumin reached in colorectal tissue in patients following a 14-day course. Twenty-eight patients with colorectal cancer were recruited in the clinical trial. Each subject was orally administered 2.35 g of Curcumin for 14 days. Mucosal biopsies were collected at endoscopy (sampling time post dose 14-39.5 h); plasma and urine sample (6.5-35.5 h) were collected post Curcumin dose. This clinical study also included a novel method of pharmacokinetic analysis, which measured the tissue levels of Curcumin both before and after the tissue has been washed copiously with aqueous salt solution. Results from the clinical study showed that detectable Curcuminoids were observed in the urine sample of

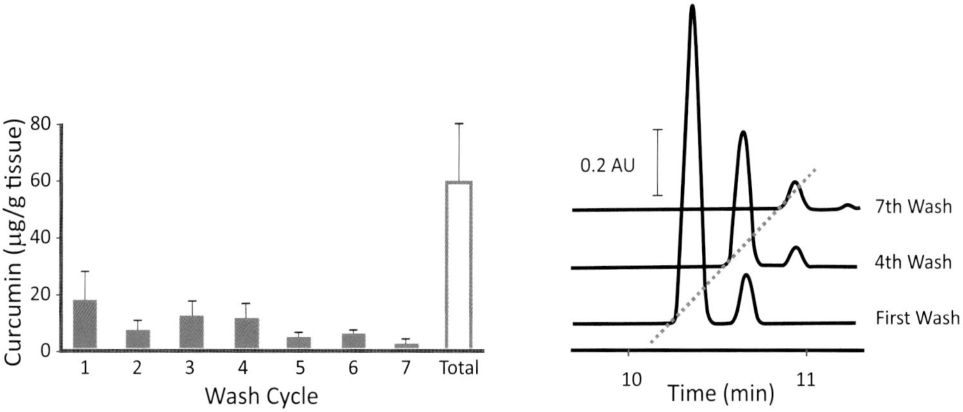


**Fig. 9:** (a) Mean Curcumin (in µg/g) present in consecutive washes (in orange bars) and cumulative Curcumin removed during wash cycles (white bar)
(b) UPLC-UV chromatography of samples from series washes performed to isolate the Curcumin from colonic mucosa

all participants. Further, pharmacologically active levels of Curcuminoids were recovered from bowel mucosa even after multiple tissue washes (Fig. 9), which supports the safety of Curcumin and its potential usefulness in long term colorectal cancer prevention strategies. The Curcumin regimen at this dosage was also found to be safe with no serious side effects. This trial is also the first for monitoring the attitude of cancer patients towards oral Curcumin supplementation, which provided important information for future trials on its long term use (2/3rd of patients recommended use of Curcumin) [Irving *et al*. 2013].

Benefits of Curcumin C3 Complex® have been evaluated both in the preliminary stage of cancer initiation, where aberrant crypt foci (ACF) forms in the lining of colon and rectum and in the advanced stages of colorectal polyp development. While the above two studies proved the beneficial effects of Curcumin C3 Complex® in preventing polyp formation, a separate study has been carried out for its role in preventing initial stages of colorectal cancer.

Phase IIa Clinical Trial of Curcumin for the Prevention of Colorectal Neoplasia

## Phase IIa clinical trial of curcumin for the prevention of colorectal neoplasia

Carroll *et al.*

*Cancer Prev Res.* 2011

Researchers at University of Illinois, Chicago, USA conducted a clinical trial on 44 subjects, who had 8 or more rectal aberrant crypt foci (ACF) and had a history of smoking for at least 3 years. Researchers wanted to see the effect of Curcuminoids on the ACF and levels of carcinogens such as prostaglandins (PGE2) and 5-hydroxyeicosatetraenoic acid (5-HETE). This trial was conducted in 2 stages of 30 days supplementation in each stage. In the first stage Curcumin was supplemented at 2 g once daily and in the second stage 4 g once daily. The protocol required to find the acceptable toxicity before initiating the second stage. At the end of each stage, the plasma and tissue biopsies were collected. Results showed a significant reduction in the ACF number. Interestingly, this effect was not observed with any significant changes in the PGE2 and 5-HETE levels. This study concluded that the levels of COX or LOX enzyme do not correlate to ACF reduction. Further, Curcumin may mediate anticarcinogenic effects via alternative signaling pathways or via inhibition of upstream events. Above clinical study further validated the earlier findings on the effect of Curcumin C3 Complex® on colon health [Carroll *et al.* 2011].

Combination Treatment With Curcumin and Quercetin of Adenomas in Familial Adenomatous Polyposis

# Combination treatment with curcumin and quercetin of adenomatous polyposis

Cruz-Correa *et al.*

*Clin Gastroenterol Hepato.* 2006

Familial adenomatous polyposis (FAP) is an autosomal dominant form of hereditary colorectal cancer, in which hundreds of colorectal adenomas develop in adolescent age with potentially developing into colorectal cancer in later stage of life unless the polyps are removed.

Earlier studies on the FAP showed decrease in adenomas with use of Sulindac and Celecoxib (COX-2 selective inhibitors). Though the effective regression was observed using the above drugs, the side effects from these chemopreventive drugs limit their use as a first choice of defense. Hence, there is a need for natural chemopreventive drugs for the effective management of FAP with less side effects. While the benefits of Curcumin is evident from the clinical studies done on colorectal cancer, another natural compound which has been investigated for its effect on colon cancer is quercetin. Quercetin belongs to polyphenolic family and is present in nature in onion, green tea and St. John's wort. It is also a principal constituent observed in red wine. Quercetin has been studied for its antioxidant activity and has been of interest in colon health management as *ex vivo* studies showed inhibition of cell growth in human colon cancer cells.

A clinical study was conducted by researchers at Johns Hopkins University School of Medicine, Maryland, USA on subjects suffering from FAP using the Curcumin-quercetin combination sold as Oxy-Q tablets with Curcumin C3 Complex®. In this 9-month clinical trial, five subjects with familial adenomatous polyposis and who had undergone colectomy and had 5 or more adenomas were selected to receive 3 tablets of Oxy-Q daily, each containing 480 mg Curcumin and 20 mg of quercetin. All patients were asked to avoid taking the NSAIDs during the trial.

Safety was monitored regularly and also number and size of adenomas were evaluated during every visit at 3-month interval.

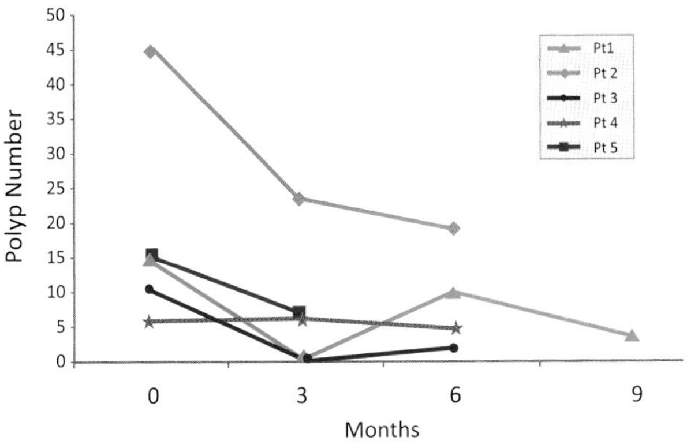


**Fig. 10:** Polyp number after treatment with Curcumin and quercetin

Results showed that Curcumin-quercetin combination was useful in the management of patients with familial adenomatous polyposis and prior colectomy as it effectively reduced the number as well as size of adenomatous polyps in both retained rectum and ileonal pouch (Fig. 10).

The study results were consistent with the effects observed in literature for use of Curcumin in colorectal carcinogenesis.

The study also showed high compliance with no serious adverse events occurring in any of the patients [Cruz-Correa *et al.* 2006].

The mechanism of anticancer activity of Curcumin included upregulation of glutathione-S-transferase, free radical scavenging and suppression of COX-2, while quercetin's anticarcinogenic activity may arise from its inhibition of p21-Ras expression in colon cancer cell lines.

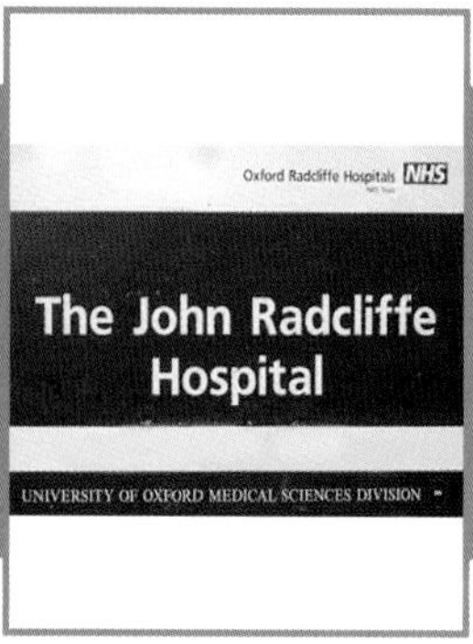


# A Case Study at John Radcliffe Hospital, Oxford

A case study was carried out on an individual (age:18 years) having over 250 polyps, where 50 of them were sessile (with no stalk) and 200 of them were pedunculated. A dose of 8 g of Curcumin C3 Complex® was given per day and at the end of six months, a significant reduction in number of polyps was observed. The number of polyps reduced to only 100 with the pedunculated polyps reducing to only 50 in number. There is a greater concern to reduce the number of pedunculated polyps since they carry a larger risk of malignancy and produce more villous components (Fig. 11).

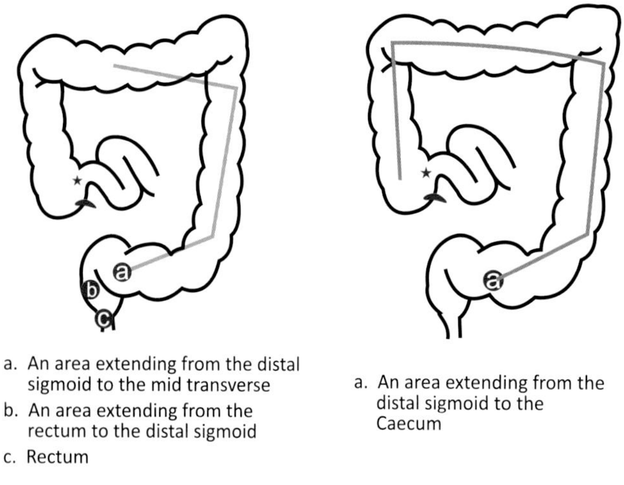

a
b
c
a
a. An area extending from the distal sigmoid to the mid transverse
b. An area extending from the rectum to the distal sigmoid
c. Rectum
a. An area extending from the distal sigmoid to the Caecum


**Fig. 11:** Images from the original medical report at study initiation and end of six months showing significant reduction in number of polyps

Colon cancer remains to be the fourth most common cancer globally. While chemotherapy is commonly advised in subjects diagnosed with colon cancer, a high rate of chemo-resistance is observed. In case of colorectal cancer the most recognized chemotherapy used is FOLFOX regimen. This regimen consists of oxaliplatin and 5-fluorouracil and folinic acid. FOLFOX has been relatively well tolerated in colon cancer patients, however, its dose-limiting side effects have been common and in some cases cause life threatening diarrhea due to mucositis. Further, majority of patients over the period of treatment develop oxaliplatin-induced neuropathy leading to cessation or dose reduction.

Curcumin's anticancer activity has been well established in various pre-clinical and clinical studies. Further studies on the combination of Curcumin and chemotherapy have shown synergistic effect on cancer cell treatment. Clinical evidences show reduction in the tumor volume and metastatic features when combined with chemotherapy.

Accepted Manuscript

Title: Curcumin inhibits cancer stem cell phenotypes in *ex vivo* models of colorectal liver metastases, and is clinically safe and tolerable in combination with FOLFOX chemotherapy

Author: Mark I. James, Chinenye Iwuji, Glen Irving, Ankur Karmokar, Jennifer A. Higgins, Nicola Griffin-Teal, Anne Thomas, Peter Greaves, Hong Cai, Samita R. Patel, Bruno Morgan, Ashley Dennison, Matthew Metcalfe, Giuseppe Garcea, David M. Lloyd, David P. Berry, William P. Steward, Lynne M. Howells, Karen Brown

| | |
|---|---|
| PII: | S0304-3835(15)00326-2 |
| DOI: | http://dx.doi.org/doi:10.1016/j.canlet.2015.05.005 |
| Reference: | CAN 12401 |
| To appear in: | *Cancer Letters* |
| Received date: | 13-3-2015 |
| Revised date: | 16-4-2015 |
| Accepted date: | 4-5-2015 |

Please cite this article as: Mark I. James, Chinenye Iwuji, Glen Irving, Ankur Karmokar, Jennifer A. Higgins, Nicola Griffin-Teal, Anne Thomas, Peter Greaves, Hong Cai, Samita R. Patel, Bruno Morgan, Ashley Dennison, Matthew Metcalfe, Giuseppe Garcea, David M. Lloyd, David P. Berry, William P. Steward, Lynne M. Howells, Karen Brown, Curcumin inhibits cancer stem cell phenotypes in *ex vivo* models of colorectal liver metastases, and is clinically safe and tolerable in combination with FOLFOX chemotherapy., *Cancer Letters* (2015), http://dx.doi.org/doi:10.1016/j.canlet.2015.05.005.

This is a PDF file of an unedited manuscript that has been accepted for publication. As a service to our customers we are providing this early version of the manuscript. The manuscript will undergo copyediting, typesetting, and review of the resulting proof before it is published in its final form. Please note that during the production process errors may be discovered which could affect the content, and all legal disclaimers that apply to the journal pertain.

## Curcumin inhibits cancer stem cell phenotypes in *ex vivo* models of colorectal liver metastases, and is clinically safe and tolerable in combination with FOLFOX chemotherapy

James *et al.*

*Cancer Lett.* 2015

A Phase I dose-escalation study has been carried out to assess the safety, tolerability and feasibility of administering oral Curcumin during standard FOLFOX chemotherapy for palliation of colorectal liver metastases.

Initially, 12 participants who enrolled into the study received 500 mg (1 capsule) of oral Curcumin C3 Complex®, daily for 7 days prior to the scheduled chemotherapy. Since no Curcumin-induced toxicities (CIT) were observed, the daily oral Curcumin was continued even after commencement of chemotherapy. The FOLFOX-based chemotherapy consisted of 2-weekly cycles of chemotherapy up to 12 cycles. Patients who completed two cycles of chemotherapy without reports of any Curcumin-induced toxicity were enrolled to the next improved dose of 1 g (2 capsules), daily followed by 2 g (4 capsules).

It was observed that 50% of patients completed 12 cycles of chemotherapy with Curcumin and the average compliance rate across all participants was 93.8%. Target lesions were reduced by 30% in 58.3% of the patients treated with Curcumin. The highest response observed was a 75.8% reduction in lesions. It was also recorded that majority of the patients (91.7 %) showed no adverse effects [James *et al.*2015].

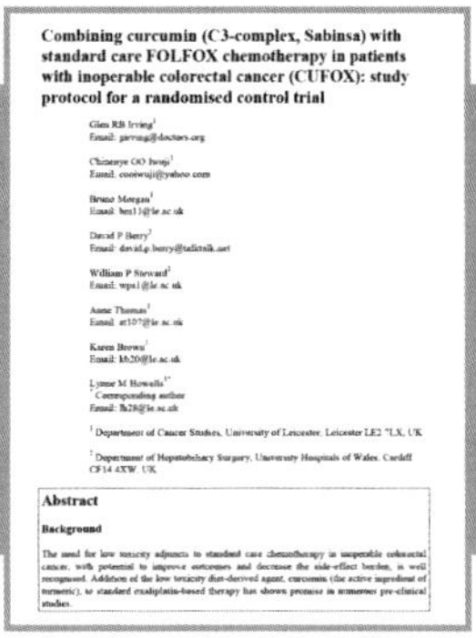

**Combining curcumin (C3-complex, Sabinsa) with standard care FOLFOX chemotherapy in patients with inoperable colorectal cancer (CUFOX): study protocol for a randomised control trial**

Glen RB Irving[1]
Email: girving@doctors.org

Chinenye OO Iwuji[1]
Email: cooiwuji@yahoo.com

Bruno Morgan[1]
Email: bm11@le.ac.uk

David P Berry[2]
Email: david.p.berry@talktalk.net

William P Steward[1]
Email: wps1@le.ac.uk

Anne Thomas[1]
Email: at107@le.ac.uk

Karen Brown[1]
Email: kb20@le.ac.uk

Lynne M Howells[1*]
* Corresponding author
Email: lh28@le.ac.uk

[1] Department of Cancer Studies, University of Leicester, Leicester LE2 7LX, UK

[2] Department of Hepatobiliary Surgery, University Hospitals of Wales, Cardiff CF14 4XW, UK

**Abstract**

**Background**

The need for low toxicity adjuncts to standard care chemotherapy in inoperable colorectal cancer, with potential to improve outcomes and decrease the side-effect burden, is well recognised. Addition of the low toxicity diet-derived agent, curcumin (the active ingredient of turmeric), to standard oxaliplatin-based therapy has shown promise in numerous pre-clinical studies.

## Combining Curcumin (C3 Complex, Sabinsa) with standard care FOLFOX chemotherapy in patients with inoperable colorectal cancer (CUFOX): Study protocol for randomized control trial

Irving *et al.*

*Trials* 2015

With the above knowledge on the benefits of Curcumin in chemotherapy [James *et al.*2015], a clinical trial has been planned by researchers at Leicester University, UK. This phase I dose-escalation clinical study will be evaluating the effects of CUFOX (Curcumin and FOLFOX) regimen on the colon cancer subjects.

The patients will be recruited based on the diagnosis of colorectal cancer who have inoperable liver metastasis. This criteria of patients inclusion was kept as the median survival for patients in unresectable colorectal liver metastases with chemotherapy for only 24 months.

The product of choice for this clinical trial is Curcumin C3 Complex® from Sabinsa Corporation.

This clinical study will be conducted in Phase I (dose-escalation study for CUFOX) and Phase II randomized, controlled trial combining Curcumin and FOLFOX in patients with diagnosis of metastasis colorectal cancer. As the side effects of this combination are unknown, a dose-escalation study is planned as mentioned above. Curcumin will be administered in a dosage of 0.5-2.0 g per day. The target dosage of Curcumin has been chosen based on the compliance from a pilot study. Further, in an animal model study, polyp prevention demonstrating efficacy for Curcumin proposes use of 1.6 g per day delivered in a single dosage in human.

The primary endpoints in this clinical study will be to measure safety and tolerability of the FOLFOX-Curcumin combination.

This will be the first clinical trial to investigate the outcomes from the combination of oral Curcumin with standard care oxaliplatin-based chemotherapy. CUFOX is a first randomized trial of its kind and results of this trial can provide early evidence of clinical efficacy of Curcumin within the chemotherapeutic setting [Irving *et al.* 2015].

# Breast Cancer

Breast cancer is one of the most common type of cancer in women, across any race or ethnicity and is one of the leading causes of death from cancer in women. In the US 220,097 women were diagnosed with breast cancer in 2011, the death alone with this cancer numbered more than 40,000 as per the data from Center for Disease Control (CDC). Depending on the kind of breast cancer and how far it is spread, different treatments are recommended including hormonal therapy, chemotherapy, surgery or radiation therapy. Current drug used in the treatment regimen is docetaxel, which is a mitotic inhibitor promoting microtubule assembly. It prevents tubulin depolymerization and results in failed cell division and cytotoxicity due to arresting cells at G2/M transition.

We have seen that anticancer benefits of Curcumin arise from its anti-inflammatory, antiproliferative and apoptotic effects. In previous studies on various cancers, Curcuminoids have shown to increase the sensitivity of cancer cells towards the existing drug therapies such as doxorubicin, tamoxifen, cisplastin etc. Based on some of the earlier pre-clinical studies on breast cancer cells, a clinical study focusing on evaluating the safety and potentiating effect of Curcumin on docetaxel drug regimen was planned.

Phase I dose escalation trial of docetaxel plus curcumin in patients with advanced and metastatic breast cancer

## Phase I dose escalation trial of docetaxel plus curcumin in patients with advanced and metastatic breast cancer

Bayet-Robert *et al.*

*Cancer Biol Ther*. 2010

Researchers at University of Auvergne Centre d'Investigation Clinique, France conducted a clinical trial to evaluate the role of Curcumin supplementation on breast cancer patients, who were on docetaxel (100 mg/m$^2$) regimen. In this open-label, Phase I trial, 14 eligible subjects who had metastatic or advanced breast cancer were administered docetaxel at dose of 100 mg/m$^2$ 1 h perfusion, every 3 weeks for 6 cycles with total 63 cycles. These patients received Curcumin 500 mg/day for seven consecutive days at each cycle from day -4 to day +2 of therapy.

As a primary end-point, maximum tolerable dosage of the Curcumin was determined. In the Phase I trial, 6 dose levels of Curcumin were evaluated (500 mg, 1000 mg, 2000 mg, 4000 mg, 6000 mg and 8000 mg) for dose-related toxicities. The maximum tolerable dose was found to be 8000 mg/day in patients suffering from breast cancer. No incidence of toxicity was observed on this tested combination, which included monotherapy of docetaxel. Curcumin/docetaxel combination demonstrated antitumor activity.

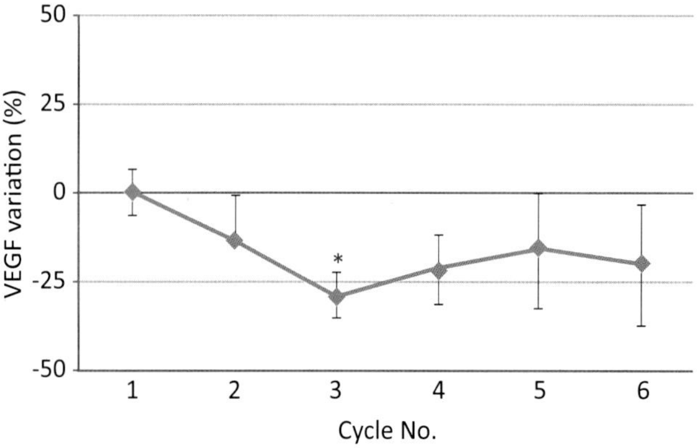


**Fig. 12:** Antiangiogenic VEGF marker as percentage of baseline across 6 cycles of treatment in 8 patients with measurable lesions

The antiangiogenic activity of the

combination was evaluated with the vascular endothelial growth factor expression and it was found that Curcumin/docetaxel combination reduced the expression of vascular endothelial growth factor after three cycles of treatment (Fig. 12). One more aspect which researchers mentioned was on the potential role of Curcumin in reducing the tumor cell resistance towards docetaxel, where Curcumin could improve systemic bioavailability of the drug due to its effect on P-glycoprotein in the gut lining.

The study concluded with positive results on the safety and efficacy of Curcumin C3 Complex® combination with docetaxel drug therapy regimen in advanced and metastatic breast cancer patients [Bayet-Robert *et al.* 2010].

# Non-Hodgkin's Lymphoma

Non-Hodgkin's Lymphoma (NHL) is a cancer that originates in the lymphatic system and can spread rapidly throughout the body. In Non-Hodgkin's Lymphoma, tumors develop from lymphocytes, a type of white blood cells. Non-Hodgkin's lymphoma is the seventh most common cancer in the US with estimate of 584,000 people living with it. As per 2007-2011 data from National Cancer Institute, there were about 19.7 cases of Non-Hodgkin's Lymphoma per 100,000 adults per year and 6.3 deaths per 100,000 adults per year. It was also estimated that about 2.1% of men and women will be diagnosed with Non-Hodgkin's Lymphoma at some point during their lifetime. There are many different types of Non-Hodgkin's Lymphoma. These types can be divided into aggressive (fast-growing) and indolent (slow-growing) types and they can be formed from either B cells or T cells. Follicular lymphoma accounts for 20% of cases of lymphoma in the US, affecting the B cells and considered as a slow-growing lymphoma. The characteristic feature of follicular lymphoma is that cells grow in circular pattern in lymph nodes, with common sign of disease that includes enlargement of lymph glands in neck, underarm, groin, fatigue, weight loss, shortness of breath etc. Though often people with follicular lymphoma may show no apparent symptoms when diagnosed, 30-40% of patients with lymphoma may eventually develop into aggressive lymphoma and require chemotherapy.

Treatment of symptoms is an acceptable approach, however, follicular lymphoma is considered incurable using this approach, which has limitations including relapses.

Oxidation-reduction (REDOX) signaling system has been suggested as an important target in cancer. One of the proteins in this REDOX signaling system, AP endonuclease 1 (APE1)/Ref-1 is of great interest in B cell follicular lymphoma. AP endonuclease 1 is a key enzyme in base excision repair (BER) pathway, thus helping the DNA repair and survival of cells. However, in cancer cells such activity may lead to increased therapeutic resistance of cancer cells against DNA damage caused by regular chemotherapeutic/ionization treatments, thus negatively affecting on the outcome of such therapeutic pathways in cancer treatments. Elevated levels of AP endonuclease 1 are indicators of chemotherapeutic resistance. AP endonuclease 1 also induces the COX-2 expression through the activation of NF-κB.

**Curcumin and EGCG Suppress Apurinic/Apyrimidinic Endonuclease 1 and Induce Complete Remission in B-cell Non-Hodgkin's lymphoma Patients**

**Ahmad R. Bassiouny[1], Mona A. Atteya[1], Fatma H. El-Rashidy[1], Hashem M. Neenaa[2]**

[1]Department of Biochemistry, Faculty of Science, Alexandria University, Egypt; [2]Department of Internal Medicine, Hematological Disease Unit, Faculty of Medicine, Alexandria University, Egypt

**Corresponding author:** Ahmad R. Bassiouny, PhD, Professor, Department of Biochemistry, Faculty of Science, Alexandria University, Egypt

Submission date: November 2, 2011; Acceptance date: December 12, 2011; Publication date: December 30, 2011

ABSTRACT:

**Background**: Follicular lymphoma (FL) is the most common subtype of indolent lymphoma. FL is still considered to be an incurable disease and palliation of symptoms is an acceptable approach to the expected pattern of repeated relapses due to developing resistance to chemotherapy agents. Apurinic/apyrimidinic endonuclease/redox factor-1 (APE1/Ref-1) is a multifunctional protein involved in DNA base excision repair (BER) of oxidative DNA damage and in redox regulation of a number of transcription factors. It was observed that cytoplasmic APE1 induced COX-2 expression through NF-κB activation. It has been shown that chemopreventive agents potentiate the efficacy of chemotherapy through the regulation of multiple signaling pathways, including NF-κB, c-Myc, cyclooxygenase-2, apoptosis, and others, suggesting a multitargeted nature of chemopreventive agents. We hypothesized that curcumin, a polyphenolic antioxidant derived from the spice turmeric, and epigallocatechin gallate (EGCG) from green tea would potentiate the effect of chemotherapy in B-cell lymphoma.

**Objective:** We examined the role of human apurinic/apyrimidinic endonuclease 1 (APE1) in resistance and prognosis in patients with FL. Our major objective was to update the safety and efficacy results of the antitumor effect of combination of curcumin and EGCG therapy in relapsed or resistant indolent or transformed non-Hodgkin follicular lymphoma patients and their peripheral blood mononuclear cells (PBMCs) compared with healthy donors' controls.

**Methods:** Thirty patients with FL with over-expression of constitutive active NF-κB in their PBMCs received regular CHOP and consumed capsules compatible with curcumin doses between 0.9 and 5.4 g daily for up to 9 months and 9.0 g/day green tea whole extract "1000 mg tablets of green tea whole extract containing 200 mg EGCG. We designed a dose-escalation

# Curcumin and EGCG Suppress Apurinic/Apyrimidinic Endonuclease 1 and Induce Complete Remission in B-cell Non-Hodgkin's lymphoma Patients

Bassiouny *et al.*

*Funct Food Health Dis.* 2011

Researchers at Alexandria University, Egypt conducted a 9-month cohort trial on 40 subjects (including 10 healthy and 30 subjects with Non-Hodgkin's Lymphoma) with a combination of Curcuminoids and epigallocatechin gallate (EGCG) containing green tea extract as an adjuvant to Cyclophosphamide, Hydroxydaunorubicin, Oncovin and Prednisone (CHOP) therapy. The dosage of the green tea was kept at 9.0 g/day; provided in 1000 mg capsules, each containing 200 mg EGCG and Curcumin was provided as Curcumin C3 Complex® capsules from America's Finest Inc. (a subsidiary group of Sabinsa) in doses between 0.9 g to 5.4 g/day for 9 months. Thirty subjects were divided in 3 groups in active treatment groups, each receiving either CHOP or CHOP-based chemotherapy with either Curcumin or Curcumin–EGCG combination for 9 months.

Blood samples were drawn from the patients at baseline and at specific intervals of 3, 6, 9 and 12 months of treatment. The effect of Curcumin/green tea combination in reducing the drug resistance in Non-Hodgkin's Lymphoma patients was estimated by determination of glutathione-S-transferase activities. Results showed that Curcumin alone or in combination with green tea extract was able to inhibit the NF-κB activity and also helped in sensitizing lymphoma patients to CHOP therapy. There was a significant reduction in serum vascular endothelial growth factor levels in subjects receiving the combination of Curcumin and EGCG. The analysis of glutathione-S-transferase showed that it was reduced in groups treated with Curcumin and EGCG. Since glutathione-S-transferase is involved in the detoxification of carcinogens, it is usually increased in most of human tumors and its high concentration detoxifies anticancer agents and increases drug resistance. By lowering glutathione-S-transferase this combination was able to overcome chemotherapy resistance in Non-Hodgkin's Lymphoma subjects. It was also observed that patients on this combination remained disease-free for a mean of 8.6 years (range= 7.9–9.2 years) after this combination therapy.

Authors of the study concluded that Curcumin and EGCG may help to reduce the drug resistance in Non-Hodgkin's Lymphoma patients and can be a part of palliative regimen in such patients [Bassiouny *et al*. 2011].

 

# Radiation Dermatitis

Radiotherapy is a part of anticancer therapy, where the malignant cells are exposed to ionizing radiation to kill or inhibit the growth of cancer cells. However, exposure to such radiation has its own side effects on healthy cells. One of the common side effects experienced by patients undergoing radiotherapy for sarcoma, breast cancer, lung, head and neck cancer is radiation dermatitis. Currently there are no standard treatments used for radiation dermatitis.

Curcumin, well known for its antioxidant and anti-inflammatory activities is also known for its benefit in the skin ailments such as scabies, acne and eczema. Its healing effect on the skin is well described in literature and because of its safe and non-toxic nature it becomes a natural choice for researchers to manage radiation dermatitis.

Curcumin for Radiation Dermatitis: A Randomized, Double-Blind, Placebo-Controlled Clinical Trial of Thirty Breast Cancer Patients

## Curcumin for radiation dermatitis: a randomized, double-blind, placebo-controlled clinical trial of thirty breast cancer patients

Ryan *et al.*

*Radiat Res.* 2013

Researchers at Department of Radiation and Oncology, University of Rochester, USA conducted a randomized, double-blind, placebo-controlled clinical trial for 4–7 weeks in breast cancer patients. All subjects were receiving the standard fractionated radiotherapy (1.8–2.4 Gy per session). Thirty subjects enrolled in this study were divided in two groups and were prescribed 6 g of Curcuminoids (in 500 mg capsules containing Curcumin C3 Complex®) to be taken as 2 g, three times a day throughout the radiation therapy. Standard care topical agents were allowed to be used including hydrocortisone creams. The radiation dermatitis severity was measured using a scale (Radiation Dermatitis Severity-RDS scoring scale), along with measurement of redness of skin, digital imaging of skin changes and a self-assessment questionnaire. The results collected from 30 subjects who completed the clinical trial showed that Curcumin administration reduced the severity of radiation dermatitis as evaluated by RDS scoring scale. Further, Fisher's exact test also showed that moist desquamation occurred in fewer patients in Curcumin group as compared to placebo group. The clinical study also showed that Curcumin C3 Complex® at the dosage decided in this clinical study were well tolerated and did not show any significant adverse events. Interestingly, while antioxidants are recommended to be avoided during radiation therapy as they can reduce the effectiveness of radiotherapy by protecting tumor cells, Curcumin sensitized the cancer cells to radiation. Thus, Curcumin can be a promising natural compound for treating cancer as well as cancer therapy-related side effects [Ryan *et al*. 2013].

# Inflammation

Today, chronic inflammation is regarded as the root cause of several chronic diseases and management of these health conditions has been focused on inhibiting the underlying inflammation. Curcumin has gained profound interest in this regard as it affects multiple targets involved in the inflammation such as downregulation of several cytokines like TNF-$\alpha$, interleukin-1, interleukin-2, interleukin-6, interleukin-8, interleukin-12, pro-inflammatory enzymes such as COX-2 and inducible nitric oxide synthase. Curcumin's role in downregulating the transcription factor (NF-κB) has brought it to forefront as NF-κB is known to regulate over 300 genes, which promote abnormal inflammatory response that can lead to variety of disorders and chronic diseases.

In the following sections, we will look at some of the applications of Curcumin C3 Complex® in various inflammatory conditions and how Curcumin supplementation can help in the management of inflammation.

# *Oral Lichen Planus (OLP)*

Lichen planus is a chronic autoimmune, mucocutaneous inflammatory disorder. It affects 1-2% of population with development of oral mucosal lesions. The exact cause is not well known, however, a spectrum of antigen-specific and non-specific mechanisms have been cited as a cause of oral lichen planus. There are several treatments which are in practice such as use of steroids topically on the surface as well as laser therapy. Therefore, the treatment options for oral lichen planus are systemic and/or topical corticosteroids, however, their effectiveness is limited by their side effects.

Curcumin was selected by researchers for evaluating its potential against oral lichen planus because of its broad-spectrum anti-inflammatory nature and safety profile.

ScienceDirect

Phytomedicine

A randomized, placebo-controlled, double-blind clinical trial of curcuminoids in oral lichen planus

# A randomized, placebo-controlled, double-blind clinical trial of curcuminoids in oral lichen planus

Chainani-Wu *et al.*

*Phytomedicine* 2007

In this randomized, double-blind, placebo-controlled clinical trial conducted at University of California, San-Francisco, USA the effect of Curcumin supplementation (Curcumin C3 Complex®) was studied for oral lichen planus. Thirty-three patients with oral lichen planus were recruited for the study and divided in two groups to receive either 60 mg of prednisone/day for the first week and 2000 mg of Curcuminoids/day in divided dosage for 7 weeks or 60 mg of prednisone/day for the first week and matching placebo for 7 weeks. Effect of Curcumin was measured using Visual Analog Scale (VAS) and a Modified Oral Mucositis Index (MOMI). Curcumin was found to be well tolerated at the dosage of 2000 mg/day with no significant adverse effects arising from Curcumin supplementation. Based on the interim results it was decided to conduct a future trial with longer follow-up and higher dosage of Curcumin [Chainani-Wu *et al.* 2007].

## High-dose curcuminoids are efficacious in the reduction in symptoms and signs of oral lichen planus

Chainani-Wu *et al.*

*J Am Acad Dermatol.* 2012a

Based on the results from the previous clinical trial done [Chainani-Wu *et al.* 2007], researchers at University of California, USA who were also involved in the previous study redesigned the clinical protocol to include 6000 mg/day dosage of Curcumin C3 Complex® to be taken for 2 weeks. Twenty subjects with oral lichen planus score in the range of 3–8 were included in this randomized, double-blind, placebo-controlled, 2-week study. An investigational new drug approval number was obtained from the USFDA. The subjects were divided in two groups (n=10), the active group was administered 6000 mg in 3 divided doses daily for 2 weeks and other group received matching placebo. In accordance with the above objectives oral lichen planus signs and symptoms were measured by using Numerical Rating Scale (NRS) and Modified Oral Mucositis Index (MOMI). Complete blood count, liver enzymes, C-reactive protein (CRP) and interleukin-6 levels were also measured. Primary outcome measure was change in symptom scores from baseline to 2-week follow-up; secondary outcome measures were changes in clinical signs, CRP and interleukin-6 from baseline and occurrence of adverse effects. Results of the clinical study showed that the Curcuminoids group showed greater reduction in the oral lichen planus symptoms as measured by NRS, erythema, ulceration and MOMI score. Curcumin C3 Complex® was also well tolerated at the recommended dose levels of 6000 mg/day [Chainani-Wu *et al.* 2012a].

This study was significant as it was the first to show that Curcuminoids were effective and safe for use in the management of oral lichen planus and also paved way for future studies on other autoimmune disorders using Curcumin C3 Complex®. Following the above study another retrospective cohort study was performed at the University of California, USA to evaluate the safety and efficacy of long term use of Curcuminoids in patients with oral lichen planus.

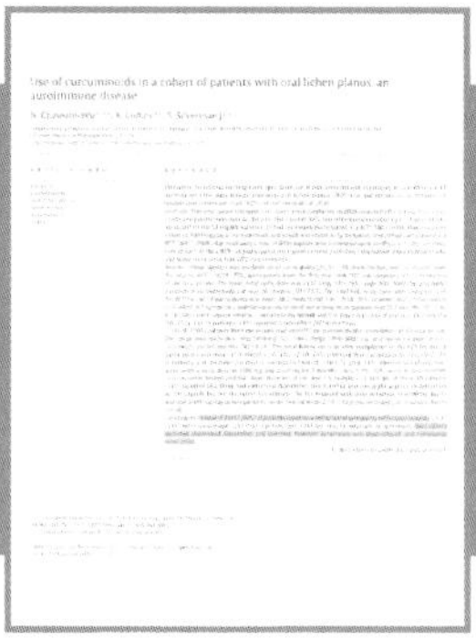

## Use of curcuminoids in a cohort of patients with oral lichen planus, an autoimmune disease

Chainani-Wu *et al.*

*Phytomedicine* 2012b

In this cohort study, subjects were included based on the use of over-the-counter (OTC) supplement containing Curcuminoids during 1-5 years of follow-up. Out of 53 subjects recruited for the study, 33 subjects were from the previous trial [Chainani-Wu *et al.* 2007] that evaluated 2000 mg/day dosage of Curcuminoids and 20 were from the clinical trial using 6000 mg/day of Curcumin C3 Complex® [Chainani-Wu *et al.* 2012b]. From the follow-up of 43 subjects, below points were summarized:

- Data was available from 75% subjects recruited in 2007 study using 2000 mg/day Curcumin and 95% subjects recruited in 2012 study using 6000 mg/day Curcumin
- From 2007 clinical trial 72% participants (n=18) took OTC Curcuminoids with mean dose of 2137.5 mg for mean duration of 30 months. Out of 18 subjects, 10 reported that Curcuminoids controlled oral lichen planus symptoms
- From 2012 clinical trial 100% participants (n=19) took OTC Curcuminoids with mean dose of 5058 mg for mean duration of 15.8 months. Twelve subjects in this group reported that the supplementation with Curcuminoids controlled oral lichen planus

From the above cohort clinical study researchers found that majority of patients reported reduction of symptoms with Curcuminoids, which validated Curcumin's long term benefit on oral lichen planus conditions and paved way for the use of Curcuminoids in the management of oral lichen planus. These studies have further fueled the interest in the use of Curcumin as a supplement in the management of other autoimmune diseases [Chainani-Wu *et al.* 2012b].

# *Psoriasis*

Psoriasis affects approximately 2% of the population of the world. It is a chronic autoimmune disease, causing patches of thick scaly skin with redness, mostly affecting the skin of elbows, neck, face, palms, soles resulting in multiple comorbidities, decrease in quality of life (QOL), increased cardiovascular risk and mortality. It can also lead to psoriatic arthritis, which affects 10-20% of the people with psoriasis. The most common type of psoriasis is plaque psoriasis. The treatment options available for psoriasis are either expensive or on long term use may increase the risk of malignancies.

As the inhibitory role of Curcumin on certain immune pathways such as NF-$\kappa$B, TNF-$\alpha$ and interferon-$\gamma$ became more evident its use in psoriasis gained more interest. However, there was lack of any controlled clinical trial regarding the use of Curcumin in psoriasis patients. Researchers at University of Pennsylvania School of Medicine, USA conducted a clinical trial to evaluate the role of Curcumin in the management of psoriasis in an effort to develop a safe and effective natural antipsoriatic therapy.

**Oral curcumin in the treatment of moderate to severe psoriasis vulgaris: A prospective clinical trial**

## Oral Curcumin in the treatment of moderate to severe *Psoriasis vulgaris*: A prospective clinical trial

Kurd *et al.*

*J Am Acad Dermatol*. 2008

In an open-label, 16-week, single-arm, non-controlled, Phase II clinical trial, 12 subjects suffering from chronic plaque psoriasis (PASI score or Psoriasis Area Severity Index of 2), 4.5 g of Curcumin C3 Complex® in 3 divided doses was administered, safety and efficacy of the Curcuminoids was investigated. The results of this study suggested that Curcumin was well tolerated by the psoriatic patients with no serious side effects, no drop-outs due to any study-related adverse events and a few subjects showing excellent response to the Curcuminoids oral therapy as indicated by Physicians Global Assessment (PGA) change at week-12.

Patients showed excellent responses of 83-88% in PASI score in week-12. Authors of the study suggested conducting a bigger trial and also use of bioavailability enhancer for better results for topical psoriasis [Kurd *et al.* 2008].

 

# *Treating Health Hazards on Exposure to Toxic Chemicals such as Sulphur Mustard*

Sulphur mustard (SM) or chemically known as bis (2-chloroethyl) sulphide is a chemical warfare agent, which was the most widely used chemical weapon in the past century. While its deployment is banned, its unlawful use in warfare has rendered several thousands of soldiers sick and injured. An example of the harmful results of this chemical was seen during the 8 years of Iran–Iraq conflict, where more than 100,000 soldiers were injured. Cutaneous complications of sulphur mustard like pruritus are acute and chronic, and persist for a long time causing other chronic complications in the respiratory system and caused histopathological changes in the lung tissue known as "**mustard lung**". In the available published literature, oxidative stress has been shown to play a role in pathogenesis of acute and chronic complications of sulphur mustard. Treatment options available for sulphur mustard-induced pruritus includes topical corticosteroids, which on long term use may give rise to several side effects. As the role of Curcumin in oxidative stress and inflammation has already been established in previously published studies, researchers at Baqiyatallah University of Medical Sciences, Tehran, Iran conducted a series of clinical trials to evaluate the safety and efficacy of Curcumin supplementation in the management of the sulphur mustard complications such as chronic pruritus.

Improvement of sulphur mustard-induced chronic pruritus, quality of life and antioxidant status by curcumin: results of a randomised, double-blind, placebo-controlled trial

## Improvement of sulphur mustard – induced chronic pruritus, quality of life and antioxidant status by curcumin: results of a randomized double blind, placebo controlled trial

Panahi *et al.*

*Br J Nutr*. 2012a

In this randomized, double-blind, placebo-controlled, 4-week clinical trial, 96 Iranian veterans aged 37-59 years suffering from chronic pruritic skin lesions induced by sulphur mustard exposure were enrolled. The subjects were divided in two groups of 46 subjects each to receive either 1 g Curcumin daily in the form of capsules of 500 mg with 5 mg of BioPerine® or matching placebo. These subjects were exposed to sulphur mustard 20 years ago and have been treated with decontamination and/or antibiotics in the first stage. Blood samples were collected at baseline and at the end of the trial, and assessment of the Curcumin supplementation was made on three scales; Visual Analogue Scale (VAS), pruritus score and Scoring atopic dermatitis Index (SCORAD).

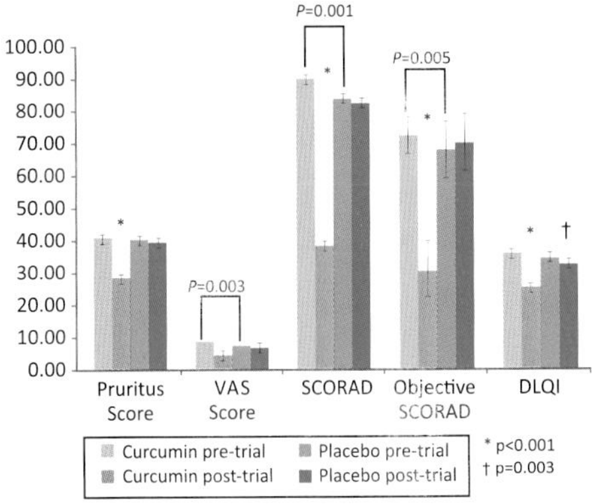


**Fig. 13:** Pre-trial vs. post-trial of evaluated efficacy measures in Curcumin and placebo groups. VAS (Visual Analogue Scale); SCORAD (Scoring atopic dermatitis); DLQI (Dermatology Life Quality Index)

Results of the trial showed that Curcumin C3 Complex® supplementation significantly increased the activity of antioxidant enzymes, which helps to fight the oxidative stress. Oxidative stress plays an important role in pathogenesis of sulphur mustard complications. Curcumin supplementation also reduced the serum substance P, which is an important mediator in pruritus. As a result, there was a marked improvement in pruritus symptoms and improved the quality of life. The outcomes measured as VAS, pruritus score and SCORAD showed a significant improvement in Curcumin group (Fig 13). The researchers concluded that results from the clinical trial clearly supported the use of Curcumin as an inexpensive treatment regimen in the management of sulphur mustard related complications and dermal toxicity [Panahi *et al.* 2012a].

In the above study, Curcumin supplementation lead to reduction in symptoms of pruritus and oxidative stress. However, as inflammation is also a key contributor in the pathogenesis of sulphur mustard-related cutaneous complications (pruritus), researchers of this study conducted another clinical trial to evaluate whether mitigation of systemic inflammation has any role in the benefits of Curcumin supplementation.

A randomized controlled trial on the anti-inflammatory effects of curcumin in patients with chronic sulphur mustard-induced cutaneous complications

Yunes Panahi[1], Amirhossein Sahebkar[2], Shahram Parvin[1] and Alireza Saadat[3]

Abstract

Introduction

## A randomized controlled trial on the anti-inflammatory effects of Curcumin in patients with chronic sulphur mustard induced cutaneous complications

Panahi *et al.*

*Ann Clin Biochem.* 2012b

Researchers of the previous clinical trial [Panahi *et al.* 2012a] at Baqiyatallah University of Medical Sciences, Tehran, Iran conducted another clinical trial to evaluate if Curcumin supplementation helped in reducing the inflammation biomarkers and led to improvement in quality of life.

Ninety-six subjects suffering from chronic pruritus were enrolled in the 4-week clinical trial, divided in two groups and received either 2 capsules of Curcumin C3 Complex® per day each containing 500 mg of Curcumin C3 Complex® and 5 mg of BioPerine® or a matching placebo. The blood samples were collected to analyze the serum concentration of inflammatory biomarkers such as interleukin-6, interleukin-8 and hs-CRP levels in the blood and Dermatology Life Quality Index (DLQI) and pruritus severity at the baseline and at the end of the trial. Results showed that supplementation of Curcumin significantly reduced the serum interleukin-8 levels as well as hs-CRP levels. At the same time Curcumin supplementation also helped to reduce the pruritus score as seen from marked decline in the pruritus score (Fig. 14). Dermatology Life Quality Index measuring quality of life showed an improvement in quality of life assessment at the end of the trial. This trial provided clinical evidence of benefits of Curcumin supplementation in reducing the pro-inflammatory cytokines and elevated levels of hs-CRP levels, which is a sensitive marker for systemic inflammation in several dermatological diseases such as pruritus, urticaria, psoriasis etc. In this clinical study another significant finding was lowering of calcitonin gene-related peptides (CGRP) levels. This is important as CGRP can upregulate the interleukin-1 and interleukin-8, hence, inflammation and its levels are usually elevated in dermal conditions like dermatitis, pruritus etc. Thus, authors concluded that the study provided evidence for the improvement in chronic pruritus, quality of life assessment from Curcumin supplementation in sulphur mustard-induced complications [Panahi *et al.* 2012b].

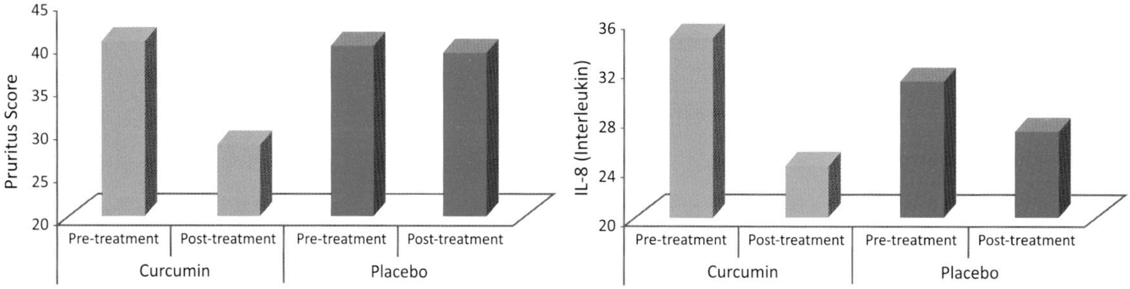


**Fig. 14:** Within-group comparison of the evaluated serum IL-8 content and pruritus score

While the dermatological complications from the sulphur mustard exposure was studied by researchers in previous two studies [Panahi *et al.* 2012a and 2012b], as continuum to the studies on the chronic complication of the sulphur mustard exposure, the group also studied the pulmonary problems. This included chronic obstructive pulmonary disease, bronchiolitis and pulmonary fibrosis caused by the exposure and also accompanied by histological changes in lung known as "mustard lung".

As we know that the oxidative stress and upregulation of inflammatory markers are commonly associated with pathology of the sulphur mustard exposure, it was also felt that the same oxidative stress may be a reason for adverse events in pulmonary tissue leading to pulmonary complications. The researchers [Panahi *et al.* 2015a] at Baqiyatallah University of Medical Sciences, Iran conducted a clinical trial on subjects suffering from the chronic pulmonary complications due to exposure to the sulphur mustard.

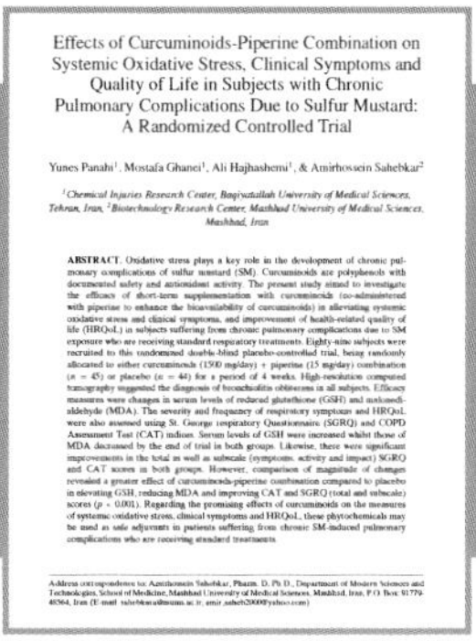

Effects of Curcuminoids-Piperine Combination on Systemic Oxidative Stress, Clinical Symptoms and Quality of Life in Subjects with Chronic Pulmonary Complications Due to Sulfur Mustard: A Randomized Controlled Trial

Yunes Panahi[1], Mostafa Ghanei[1], Ali Hajhashemi[1], & Amirhossein Sahebkar[2]

[1]*Chemical Injuries Research Center, Baqiyatallah University of Medical Sciences, Tehran, Iran,* [2]*Biotechnology Research Center, Mashhad University of Medical Sciences, Mashhad, Iran*

**ABSTRACT.** Oxidative stress plays a key role in the development of chronic pulmonary complications of sulfur mustard (SM). Curcuminoids are polyphenols with documented safety and antioxidant activity. The present study aimed to investigate the efficacy of short-term supplementation with curcuminoids (co-administered with piperine to enhance the bioavailability of curcuminoids) in alleviating systemic oxidative stress and clinical symptoms, and improvement of health-related quality of life (HRQoL) in subjects suffering from chronic pulmonary complications due to SM exposure who are receiving standard respiratory treatments. Eighty-nine subjects were recruited to this randomized double-blind placebo-controlled trial, being randomly allocated to either curcuminoids (1500 mg/day) + piperine (15 mg/day) combination ($n = 45$) or placebo ($n = 44$) for a period of 4 weeks. High-resolution computed tomography suggested the diagnosis of bronchiolitis obliterans in all subjects. Efficacy measures were changes in serum levels of reduced glutathione (GSH) and malonedialdehyde (MDA). The severity and frequency of respiratory symptoms and HRQoL were also assessed using St. George respiratory Questionnaire (SGRQ) and COPD Assessment Test (CAT) indices. Serum levels of GSH were increased whilst those of MDA decreased by the end of trial in both groups. Likewise, there were significant improvements in the total as well as subscale (symptoms, activity and impact) SGRQ and CAT scores in both groups. However, comparison of magnitude of changes revealed a greater effect of curcuminoids-piperine combination compared to placebo in elevating GSH, reducing MDA and improving CAT and SGRQ (total and subscale) scores ($p < 0.001$). Regarding the promising effects of curcuminoids on the measures of systemic oxidative stress, clinical symptoms and HRQoL, these phytochemicals may be used as safe adjuvants in patients suffering from chronic SM-induced pulmonary complications who are receiving standard treatments.

# Effects of Curcuminoids-Piperine Combinations on Systemic Oxidative Stress, Clinical Symptoms and Quality of Life in Subjects with Chronic Pulmonary Complications Due to Sulphur Mustard: A Randomized Controlled Trial

Panahi *et al.*

*J Diet Suppl.* 2015a

The effect of Curcuminoids-Piperine supplementation on the pulmonary complications in sulphur mustard-intoxicated patients receiving standard care was investigated in this randomized, double-blind, placebo-controlled clinical trial. Eighty-nine male veterans received either Curcuminoids-Piperine (1500 mg/day + 15 mg/day) combination or placebo for 4 weeks, along with the standard treatment. Blood samples were collected for determination of reduced glutathione and malondialdehyde (MDA) to evaluate the effect of Curcumin supplementation on oxidative stress. The chest high resolution computed tomography (HRCT) was performed and effects of Curcuminoids on health status of patients was evaluated using St. George Respiratory Questionnaire (SGRQ) and chronic obstructive pulmonary disease Assessment test Index.

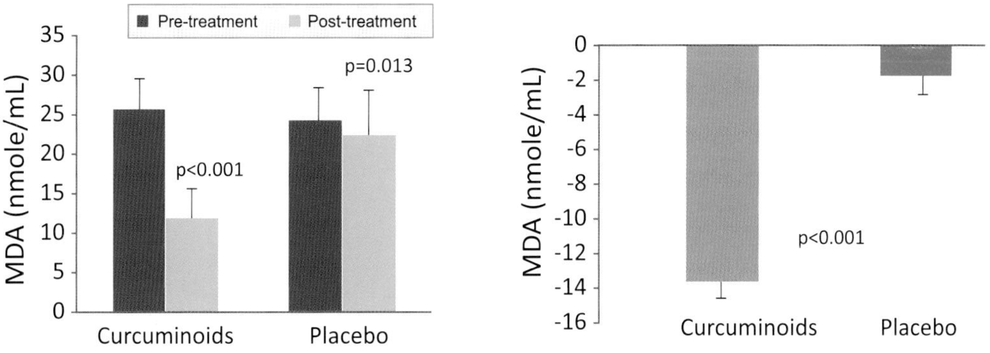


**Fig. 15:** Effect of Curcuminoids-Piperine combination vs. placebo on serum MDA concentrations. Comparison of pre vs. post-treatment values and magnitude of changes of MDA

Results of the study showed that Curcumin supplementation mitigated oxidative stress as indicated by decrease in MDA levels (Fig. 15), decreased symptoms and increased health-related quality of life in patients having sulphur mustard-induced pulmonary complications and suggested Curcuminoids as "safe adjuvants" [Panahi *et al.* 2015a]. Once again the supplementation of Curcumin C3 Complex® was found to have a potential use in treating health complications arising from exposure to toxic chemicals like sulphur mustard.

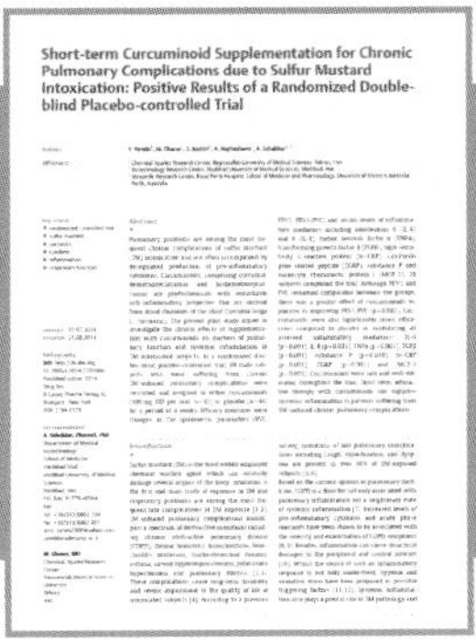
Short-term Curcuminoid Supplementation for Chronic Pulmonary Complications due to Sulfur Mustard Intoxication: Positive Results of a Randomized Double-blind Placebo-controlled Trial

## Short-term Curcuminoids Supplementation for Chronic Pulmonary Complications due to Sulfur Mustard Intoxication: Positive Results of a Randomized Double-blind Placebo-controlled Trial

Panahi *et al.*

*Drug Res.* 2014a

While another study [Panahi *et al.* 2015a] assessed the benefits of Curcumin supplementation on oxidative stress and cutaneous effects of sulphur mustard gas toxicity, the present study deals with the benefits of Curcumin supplementation on the pulmonary and systemic inflammation on sulphur mustard-intoxicated patients. Researchers at Baqiyatallah University of Medical Sciences, Tehran, Iran conducted a clinical trial to assess the clinical effects of Curcumin on pulmonary functions as well as systemic inflammation. Seventy-nine subjects suffering from documented pulmonary problems due to sulphur mustard exposure were recruited and randomized to receive either Curcumin capsules 1.5 g/day or

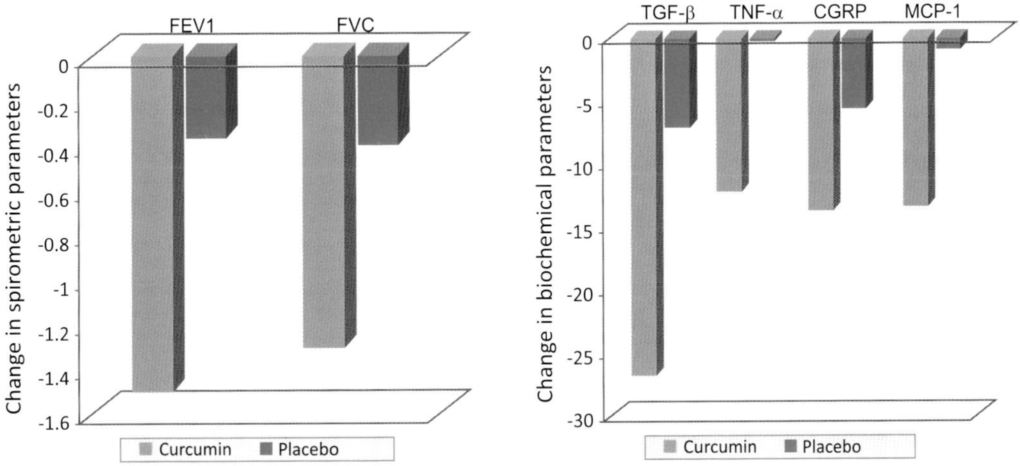


**Fig. 16:** Comparison of changes in sulphur mustard intoxicated subjects between Curcuminoids and placebo group

FEV1 - Forced Expiratory Volume in First second; FVC - Forced Vital Capacity

TGF-β - Transforming Growth Factor-β; TNF-α - Tumor Necrosis Factor - alpha

CGRP - Calcitonin Gene-related Peptide; MCP-1 - Monocyte Chemotactic Proteins-1 matching placebo. The Curcumin capsules contained Curcumin C3 Complex® (500 mg) and BioPerine® (5 mg) combination to be taken three times daily for 4 weeks. Biochemical analysis performed both at baseline and at the end of the trial included interleukin-6, interleukin-8, calcitonin gene-related peptides (CGRP), TNF-$\alpha$, monocyte chemotactic proteins-1 (MCP-1), TGF-$\beta$ and hs-CRP levels. The chest high-resolution computed tomography was performed as well as all participants underwent the spirometry to assess pulmonary function. This included measurement of forced expiratory volume in first second (FEV1) and forced vital capacity (FVC). The results showed that there was a significant decrease in the FEV1 and FCV in subjects taking Curcuminoids, showing an improvement in the pulmonary function. Interleukin-6, interleukin-8, TNF-$\alpha$, TGF-$\beta$, MCP-1 and hs-CRP levels showed a significant reduction in the Curcuminoids group (Fig 16). Thus, Curcuminoids not only showed an improvement in the pulmonary function but also reduced the inflammation in the pulmonary system. The study also showed that Curcumin was well tolerated in patients. The positive findings from this clinical study opened door for use of Curcumin in the management of respiratory diseases as an adjunct to the standard respiratory therapy in sulphur mustard toxicity. This is one of the few studies which were done on the respiratory benefits of Curcumin [Panahi *et al.* 2014a].

# Osteoarthritis (OA)

In clinical studies on the inflammatory conditions resulting from lifestyle diseases, Curcumin showed enormous benefits. One such area which has been studied using Curcumin C3 Complex® is osteoarthritis (OA). Osteoarthritis is a degenerative joint disease and is the most common type of arthritis. In osteoarthritis the protective cartilage at the end of the bone wears away with time. This causes bones under the cartilage to rub together. The friction causes pain, swelling and loss of motion of the joint. Over the time, the joint may also lose its normal shape. People with joint injury are also at the risk of developing osteoarthritis. Ongoing researches have shown that obesity could lead to osteoarthritis of knee. Current treatment for osteoarthritis is limited to use of analgesics and non-steroidal anti-inflammatory drugs (NSAIDs). The use of turmeric in Asian traditional medicine as a treatment for joint pain and inflammation has suggested its role in the management of osteoarthritis. Curcuminoids can be useful in conditions like osteoarthritis.

Researchers at Baqiyatallah University of Medical Sciences, Tehran, Iran conducted a clinical trial with Curcumin C3 Complex® and BioPerine® combination for evaluating its role in the management of knee osteoarthritis. Studies from Sabinsa Corporation and independent researchers have shown that BioPerine® can increase the bioavailability of Curcumin without compromising the safety or efficacy of the Curcuminoids.

Curcuminoid Treatment for Knee Osteoarthritis: A Randomized Double-Blind Placebo-Controlled Trial

## Curcuminoid treatment for knee osteoarthritis: a randomized double-blind placebo-controlled trial

Panahi *et al.*

*Phytother Res.* 2014b

The study was conducted by researchers at Baqiyatallah University of Medical Sciences, Tehran, Iran. The efficacy of dietary supplementation with a bioavailability-boosted preparation of Curcuminoids (Curcumin C3 Complex® with BioPerine®) in the alleviation of symptoms in patients suffering from knee osteoarthritis was tested in this randomized, double-blind, placebo-controlled, parallel-group pilot trial. Patients were administered Curcumin C3 Complex® (1500 mg/day in 3 divided doses; n=19) or matched placebo capsules (n=21) for 6 weeks. Each Curcuminoid capsule contained 5 mg of BioPerine® to enhance oral bioavailability of Curcuminoids, whereas placebo capsules contained inert starch. Randomization was carried out alternatively with a 1:1 ratio scheme. The protocol allowed subjects to use the analgesic naproxen for managing unbearable pain. Efficacy measures employed in the study were Western Ontario and McMaster Universities osteoarthritis Index (WOMAC), Visual Analogue Scale (VAS) and Lequesne's Pain Functional Index (LPFI). Results of the study showed that combination of Curcumin C3

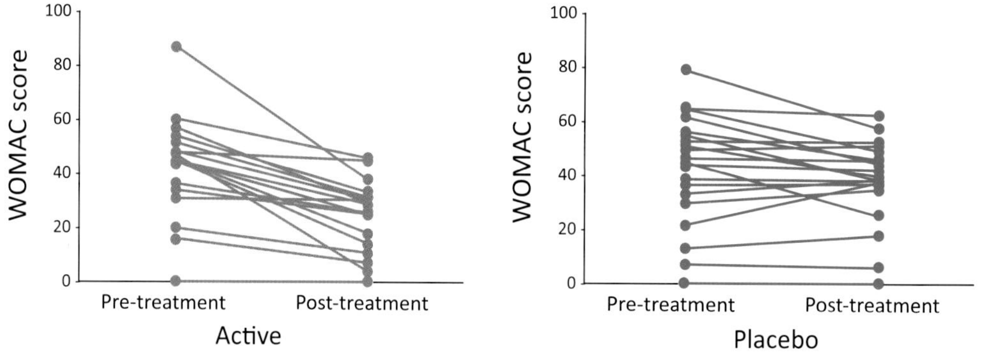


**Fig. 17A:** Intra-individual changes of WOMAC score in the Curcuminoids (left) and placebo (right) groups

Complex® with BioPerine® was very well tolerated in patients with osteoarthritis. Curcuminoids supplementation resulted in the reduction in the WOMAC scale (Fig. 17A) with a significant decrease in pain, physical function and stiffness; the LPFI and VAS scores (Fig. 17B) also showed a significant reduction. Another important finding of the study was that there was 84% decrease in the number of subjects taking naproxen in Curcuminoids group.

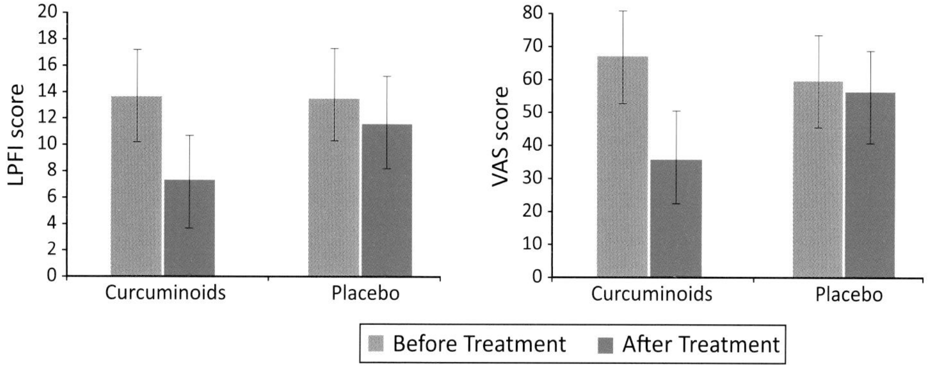


**Fig. 17B:** Changes in LPFI and VAS scores during the course of the study

This study indicated that Curcuminoids are well tolerated at the dose level of 1500 mg/day in patients with knee osteoarthritis. Results of this study showed a marked improvement in all the assessed efficacy measures, therefore, it clearly favored the efficacy of Curcuminoids in alleviating the symptoms and improving the care of patients with osteoarthritis. Thus, it can be said that Curcuminoids represent an effective and safe alternative treatment for osteoarthritis [Panahi *et al.* 2014b].

In another clinical trial [Rahimnia *et al.* 2014] of Curcumin C3 Complex® in patients with osteoarthritis has shown symptomatic relief proving its efficacy in osteoarthritis. In this sub-study, association of clinical benefits of Curcuminoids with a significant alteration in circulating biomarkers of systemic inflammation including pro-inflammatory cytokines was investigated.

 

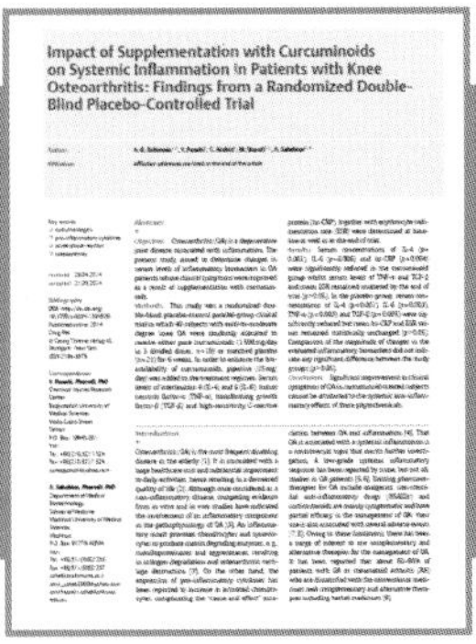
Impact of Supplementation with Curcuminoids on Systemic Inflammation in Patients with Knee Osteoarthritis: Findings from a Randomized Double-Blind Placebo-Controlled Trial

## Impact of Supplementation with Curcuminoids on Systemic Inflammation in Patients with Knee Osteoarthritis: Findings from a Randomized Double-Blind Placebo-Controlled Trial

Rahimnia *et al.*

*Drug Res.* 2014

In this sub-study, conducted at Baqiyatallah University of Medical Sciences, Tehran, Iran, researchers [Rahimnia *et al.* 2014] sought to investigate the relationship between observed clinical benefits and levels of systemic inflammatory biomarkers.

Previous study [Panahi *et al.* 2014b] showed improvement in the WOMAC, LPFI and VAS scale with Curcumin supplementation. Curcumin formulation used for clinical trial consisted of 500 mg of Curcumin C3 Complex® and 5 mg of BioPerine® capsules to be taken thrice daily. As a secondary outcome for this sub study, changes in the serum levels of interleukin-4, interleukin-6, TNF-$\alpha$, TGF-$\beta$, hs-CRP and erythrocyte sedimentation rate (ESR) were studied.

The results of this sub-study showed that systemic biomarkers of inflammation may not be correlated with the observed improvement in the symptoms of osteoarthritis. The data suggested that Curcuminoids have more beneficial effect through local anti-inflammatory mechanism in the osteo-cartilagenous tissue. Therefore, there is a need to examine the concentration of inflammatory mediators in the synovial fluid post-curcuminoid treatment.

As researchers reached to this important conclusion, another sub-study was conducted to evaluate the changes in the three important biomarkers of systemic oxidative stress following short term supplementation with Curcuminoids in patients with knee osteoarthritis.

ARTICLE

Mitigation of Systemic Oxidative Stress by Curcuminoids in Osteoarthritis: Results of a Randomized Controlled Trial

Yunes Panahi[1], Gholam Hossein Alishiri[2,**], Shahram Parvin[1], & Amirhossein Sahebkar[3,4,*]

[1]Chemical Injuries Research Center, Baqiyatallah University of Medical Sciences, Tehran, Iran, [2]Department of Internal Medicine, Faculty of Medicine, Baqiyatallah University of Medical Sciences, Tehran, Iran, [3]Biotechnology Research Center, Mashhad University of Medical Sciences, Mashhad, Iran, Neurogenic Inflammation Research Center, Mashhad University of Medical Sciences, Mashhad, Iran, [4]Metabolic Research Centre, Royal Perth Hospital, School of Medicine and Pharmacology, University of Western Australia, Perth, Australia

**ABSTRACT.** Oxidative stress is implicated in the pathogenesis of osteoarthritis. Curcuminoids are natural polyphenols with strong antioxidant capacity and may thus be helpful in the treatment of osteoarthritis. The present randomized double-blind placebo-controlled trial investigated the efficacy of curcuminoids in reducing systemic oxidative burden in patients suffering from knee osteoarthritis. Forty patients with mild-to-moderate primary knee osteoarthritis were given curcuminoid capsules (1500 mg/day in 3 divided doses; $n = 19$) or matched placebo capsules ($n = 21$) for a period of 6 weeks. Curcuminoids were co-administered with piperine (15 mg/day) in order to improve the bioavailability. Serum activities of superoxide dismutase (SOD) and concentrations of reduced glutathione (GSH) and malonedialdehyde (MDA) were determined spectrophotometrically at baseline and at the end of the treatment period in both groups. Serum activities of SOD as well as GSH and MDA concentrations were comparable between the study groups at baseline ($p > 0.05$). There was a significant elevation in serum SOD activities (mean change: $2.94 \pm 3.73$ vs. $-0.38 \pm 1.33$; $p < 0.001$), a borderline significant elevation in GSH concentrations (mean change: $1.39 \pm 2.78$ vs. $-0.02 \pm 1.62$; $p = 0.064$) and a significant reduction in MDA concentrations (mean change: $-5.26 \pm 4.46$ vs. $-2.49 \pm 3.81$; $p = 0.044$) in the curcuminoids compared with the placebo group. Changes in serum activities of SOD and concentrations of GSH and MDA during the course of trial were significantly correlated. Short-term supplementation with curcuminoids attenuates systemic oxidative stress in patients with osteoarthritis. These

# Mitigation of Systemic Oxidative Stress by Curcuminoids in Osteoarthritis: Results of a Randomized Controlled Trial

Panahi *et al.*

*J Diet Suppl.* 2015b

Oxidative stress is implicated in a variety of chronic diseases including osteoarthritis with reactive oxygen species being important contributors to extracellular matrix degradation. This sub-study was conducted to evaluate the efficacy of Curcumin supplementation in reducing the oxidative stress by measuring the levels of serum concentration of important biomarkers. This sub-study was part of the randomized, double-blind, placebo controlled, parallel group, 6-week trial. Forty subjects completed the trial, divided in two groups and were administered either 3 capsules of Curcumin C3 Complex® formulation (500 mg Curcumin C3 Complex® and 5 mg BioPerine® combination) daily or matching placebo. The primary outcome of the clinical study showed the improvement in the osteoarthritic index such as LPFI, WOMAC, VAS and improvement in stiffness, pain and increase in mobility of the joints. In this sub-study the biomarkers for oxidative stress were evaluated in both Curcumin and placebo groups. The results showed that in presence of Curcuminoids the oxidative stress was reduced significantly with increase in serum levels of superoxide dismutase (an antioxidant enzyme) and glutathione, and concurrently there was decrease in the malondialdehyde concentration. These findings further validated the antioxidant effects of Curcuminoids in chronic disease like osteoarthritis [Panahi *et al.* 2015b].

## Development of NiLitis®

As the clinical data on Curcumin showed benefits in the osteoarthritic conditions, Sabinsa also followed up on the science developing around Curcumin C3 Complex® with a multi-ingredient formulation for joint care, called NiLitis®. This formulation is unique for several reasons. Primarily, it is glucosamine free and hence, it does not have any animal-based ingredients or allergens. In addition, it is in a bilayer tablet form. Bilayer technology, though used in the pharmaceutical industry, is a very new concept in dietary supplements. Using this bilayer technology under its Integrated Nutritional Composites (INC™) umbrella of unique formulations, Sabinsa also created a multi-release formulation for the combination of Curcumin C3 Complex®, Boswellin® (*Boswellia serrata* extract), Ginger super critical fluid extract (SCFE) and BioPerine® to enhance its benefits and reduce the multiple dosing.

INTERNATIONAL JOURNAL OF PHARMACY & LIFE SCIENCES
To assess the efficacy & safety of NILIN™ SR tablets in the management of osteoarthritis of knee

# To assess the efficacy and safety of NILIN® SR tablets in the management of osteoarthritis of knee

Natarajan and Majeed.

*Int J Pharm Life Sci.* 2012

Sabinsa introduced a glucosamine-free, herb-based formulation NiLitis® SR (NILIN® SR), which aims to regenerate cartilage, reduce and manage inflammation and exert an antioxidant action. This formulation contains Curcumin C3 Complex®, Boswellin®, Gingerols and BioPerine®. A single centre, open-labeled clinical trial with 30 subjects from the age group 40-65 years having osteoarthritis of knee with no other rheumatic condition was conducted. Each patient received two tablets of NiLitis® SR tablet for oral ingestion, twice a day for 56 days. Each tablet contained Curcuminoids 250 mg, *Boswellia serrata* extract (40% AKBBA) 272 mg and Ginger extract (35% Gingerols) 100 mg. The formulation NiLitis® SR was found to be very well tolerated in patients with osteoarthritis.

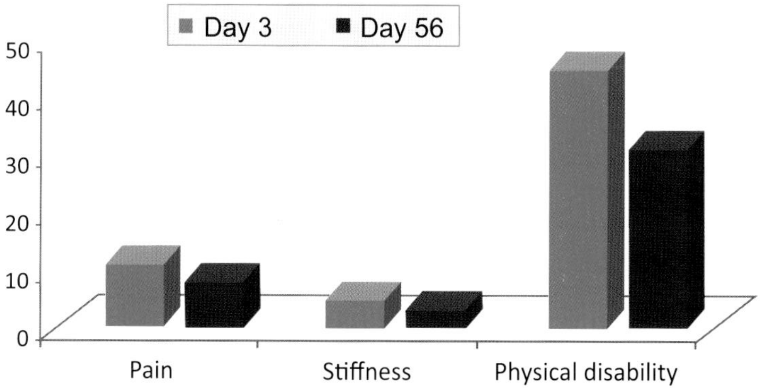


**Fig. 18:** WOMAC scores (Western Ontario and McMaster Universities) index showed a significant improvement in pain, stiffness and physical disability for patients with knee osteoarthritis

The results of the study showed a significant decrease in WOMAC score (Fig. 18), VAS (Fig. 19) and increase in six-minute walk distance (Fig. 20). From the above study it was concluded that NiLitis® SR is a safe and effective newline treatment for osteoarthritis [Natarajan and Majeed. 2012].

 

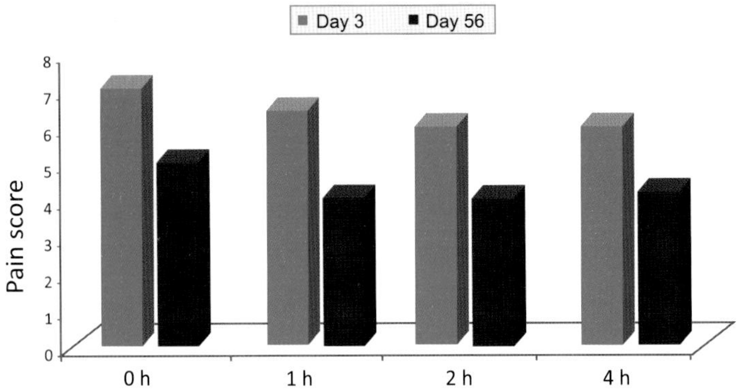


**Fig. 19:** Visual analogue scale (VAS) scores: Pain score showed a significant improvement over the course of 4 h after ingestion of the tablet from Day 6 onwards upto Day 56

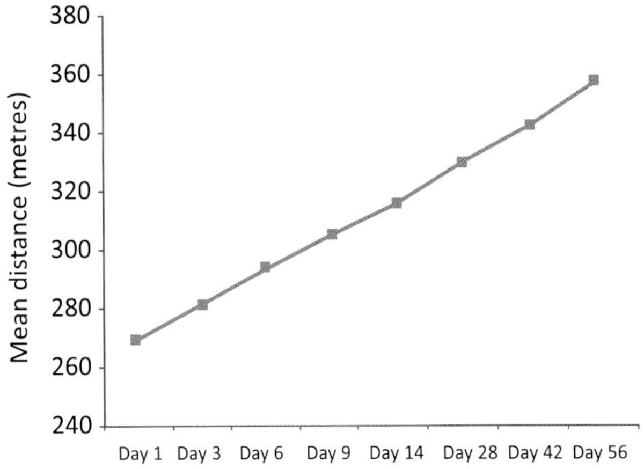


**Fig. 20:** Six-minute Walk Distance: There is a significant increase in the distance covered at each visit from the baseline

An independent clinical study on the safety and efficacy of NiLitis® SR has also been carried out in Japan. A dosage of one-tablet-per-day of NiLitis® SR showed an improvement in objective and subjective parameters as compared to the placebo. Objective parameters measured include VAS and Japanese Knee Osteoarthritis Measure (JKOM), while subjective parameters include hyaluronic acid and hs-CRP levels in serum as a measurement of inflammation. Results suggested decrease in pain as well as inflammation in patients with knee pain.

# *Oral Mucositis (OM)*

Oral mucositis (OM) is an inflammatory condition of oral cavity which arises as a complication of cancer treatment. It is caused by inflammation and necrosis of oral mucosa. The common effects of oral mucositis are pain, erythema and ulceration. Oral mucositis makes swallowing difficult and may cause serious consequences such as bleeding, reduced intake of food and even severe life threatening infection due to disruption of mucosal barrier. Palifermin, a human recombinant keratinocyte growth factor (KGF), is the only agent currently approved by the USFDA for the prevention of oral mucositis. In a previously published study [Land *et al.* 2004], Curcumin was found to prevent oral mucositis in animal models. Based on this knowledge, a clinical trial was conducted to assess the tolerability of a Curcumin mouthwash and to describe oral mucositis in pediatric patients undergoing doxorubicin-containing chemotherapy.

Topical Curcumin for the Prevention of Oral Mucositis in Pediatric Patients: Case Series

# Topical curcumin for the prevention of oral mucositis in paediatric patients: Case series

Elad *et al.*

*Altern Ther Health Med.* 2013

In a study conducted at Hadassah University Medical Center, Jerusalem, Israel, seven pediatric cancer diagnosed patients (age: 5 years or more) undergoing high dose of chemotherapy (at least 60 $mg/m^2$) were enrolled in the trial. The patients were instructed to use 10 drops of a liquid formula (a tincture of Curcumin C3 Complex®, turmeric and ginger dissolved with glycerin and 0.4% alcohol) in half a glass (50 ml) of water twice daily; (equivalent to 330 mg/day) in addition to the standard preventive oral care (chlorhexidine 0.2% mouthwash for 30 sec twice per day). Oral examination was carried out before start of the trial and then on day 7, 10, 14 and 21. Oral Mucositis Assessment Scale (OMAS) and World Health Organization (WHO) scales were used to grade the oral mucositis along with VAS scale to measure the pain. Results suggested that despite the low compliance and patients being exposed to high dosage of chemotherapy, the severity of oral mucositis caused by chemotherapy was relatively low in Curcuminoids administered subjects. The Curcumin-based mouthwash was well tolerated and was easy to use. Researchers of the study concluded that Curcumin could be used as mouthwash for the management of oral mucositis. It was also postulated that the benefits of Curcuminoids may be arising from NF-κB inhibition. Apart from its anti-inflammatory activity, Curcuminoids also possess antibacterial activity, which is useful in the management of oral health [Elad *et al.* 2013].

Part II, Chapter 7

# Cognitive Health

In recent times the understanding on inflammation has helped us to relate it to the root cause of several chronic diseases. Curcuminoids have been extensively studied for several health conditions including decline in age-related cognitive capabilities and several neuro-inflammatory diseases/health conditions such as schizophrenia, depressive disorders and Alzheimer's disease (AD). The interest in Curcuminoids was generated by the positive results from animal studies using experimental models of epileptogenesis, depression etc. Schizophrenia is considered as a serious and complex psychiatric disorder. The symptoms include false belief, confused thinking, auditory hallucinations, reduced social engagement and emotional expression. As the initial pathophysiology of schizophrenia shows increase in the oxidative stress in the brain, it was proposed that antioxidants such as Curcumin can play an important role in reducing the oxidative stress and may be beneficial in patients suffering from neuro-oxidative stress.

These findings have led to further studies on the depressive disorder conditions in human subjects.

While Alzheimer's disease was identified more than 100 years ago, research into its cause, risk factors and pathology gained momentum only in the last 20-30 years . It is estimated that 5.1 million Americans may be suffering from Alzheimer's disease, which includes half-a-million people under the age of 65 years. Alzheimer's disease today is considered as one of the most common forms of dementia, where the subject has a significant cognitive decline, which interferes with performance of everyday activities. The three stages of Alzheimer's disease are (a) preclinical Alzheimer's disease (b) mild cognitive impairment (c) dementia due to Alzheimer's disease. The pathology of Alzheimer's disease includes progressive accumulation of protein fragment beta amyloid plaques (Aβ) and twisted strands of protein Tau inside the neurons.

Curcumin having biphenolic structure binds to amyloid plaques *in vivo*, prevents Aβ-induced toxicity *in vitro* and aggregation of Aβ into fibrils. It was postulated that due to its role as an antioxidant and anti-inflammatory agent Curcumin may play an important role in the pathogenesis of Alzheimer's disease.

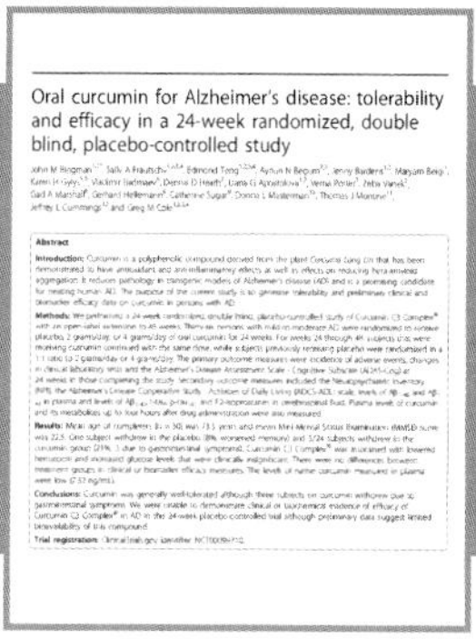
Oral curcumin for Alzheimer's disease: tolerability and efficacy in a 24-week randomized, double blind, placebo-controlled study

## Oral curcumin for Alzheimer's disease: tolerability and efficacy in a 24-week randomized, double-blind, placebo-controlled study

Ringman *et al.*

*Alzheimer's Res Ther*. 2012

Researchers at UCLA, University of California, Mary S Easton Center for Alzheimer's Disease Research, USA conducted a 24-week, randomized, double-blind, placebo-controlled, clinical trial to assess Curcumin C3 Complex® tolerability and efficacy in subjects suffering from mild-to-moderate Alzheimer's disease symptoms. The study was designed to include open-label extension to 48 weeks. Subjects suffering from dementia were diagnosed based on the DSM-IV (Diagnostic and Statistical Manual of Mental Disorders) criteria and 36 patients with probable Alzheimer's disease were enrolled in the study. Subjects were divided in three groups to receive either 2 g or 4 g Curcumin C3 Complex® per day in 2 divided dosages or matching placebo. Primary outcome was measured as tolerability of Curcuminoids and also cognitive markers. Thirty subjects completed the study. The results from the study, as a primary outcome, showed that supplementation of Curcumin in geriatric subjects at the dosage of 2 g and 4 g was well tolerated and future studies can be carried out for the use of Curcumin in the management of Alzheimer's disease with possible longer duration of the trial [Ringman *et al.* 2012].

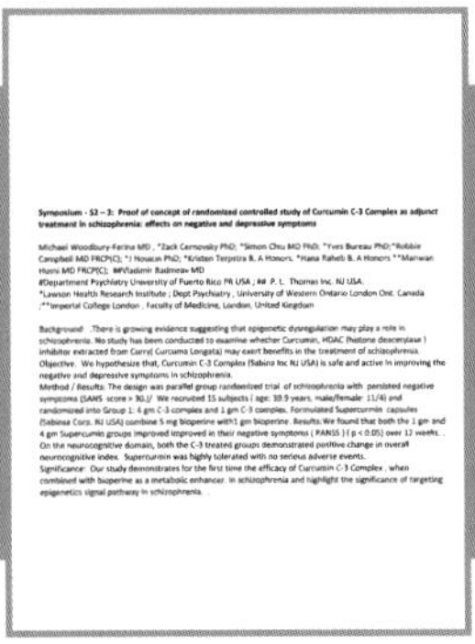

**Symposium - S2 – 3: Proof of concept of randomized controlled study of Curcumin C-3 Complex as adjunct treatment in schizophrenia: effects on negative and depressive symptoms**

Michael Woodbury-Farina MD , *Zack Cernovsky PhD; *Simon Chu MD PhD; *Yves Bureau PhD;*Robbie Campbell MD FRCP(C); *J Housain PhD; *Kristen Terpstra B. A Honors. *Hana Raheb B. A Honors **Marwan Husni MD FRCP(C); ##Vladimir Badmeav MD
#Department Psychiatry University of Puerto Rico PR USA ; ## P. L. Thomas Inc. NJ USA.
*Lawson Health Research Institute ; Dept Psychiatry , University of Western Ontario London Ont. Canada ;**Imperial College London , Faculty of Medicine, London, United Kingdom

Background: .There is growing evidence suggesting that epigenetic dysregulation may play a role in schizophrenia. No study has been conducted to examine whether Curcumin, HDAC (histone deacetylase ) inhibitor extracted from Curry( Curcuma Longata) may exert benefits in the treatment of schizophrenia.
Objective: We hypothesize that, Curcumin C-3 Complex (Sabina Inc NJ USA) is safe and active in improving the negative and depressive symptoms in schizophrenia.
Method / Results: The design was parallel group randomized trial of schizophrenia with persisted negative symptoms (SANS score > 30.)/ We recruited 15 subjects ( age: 39.9 years, male/female: 11/4) and randomized into Group 1: 4 gm C-3 complex and 1 gm C-3 complex. Formulated Supercurmin capsules (Sabinsa Corp. NJ USA) combine 5 mg bioperine with1 gm bioperine. Results:We found that both the 1 gm and 4 gm Supercumin groups improved improved in their negative symptoms ( PANSS ) ( p < 0.05) over 12 weeks. . On the neurocognitive domain, both the C-3 treated groups demonstrated positive change in overall neurocognitive index. Supercurmin was highly tolerated with no serious adverse events.
Significance: Our study demonstrates for the first time the efficacy of Curcumin C-3 Complex , when combined with bioperine as a metabolic enhancer, in schizophrenia and highlight the significance of targeting epigenetics signal pathway in schizophrenia. .

## Proof of concept of randomized controlled study of Curcumin C3 Complex® as adjunct treatment in schizophrenia: effects of negative and depressive symptoms

Woodbury-Farina *et al.*

*Symposium Cultivating Natural Bioactives: International Conference* 2012

The efficacy of Curcumin C3 Complex® when combined with BioPerine®, a nutrient bioavailability enhancer, was observed in a clinical trial on 15 subjects showing schizophrenia with persisting negative symptoms. This study also highlighted the significance of targeting epigenetics signal pathway in schizophrenia. The result of the study showed that both 1 g as well as 4 g Curcumin groups improved in the symptoms over 12 weeks. On the neurocognitive domain, Curcumin C3 Complex® treated groups demonstrated positive change in overall neurocognitive index. Curcumin was very well tolerated by the patients and no serious adverse events were observed. Therefore, use of Curcumin C3 Complex® was found to be safe and effective in improving the negative and depressive symptoms in patients suffering from schizophrenia [Woodbury-Farina *et al.* 2012].

Major depressive disorder (MDD) is another neurological disorder, which is associated with irritable moods, impairment of quality of life due to disrupted sleep, loss of motivation, fatigue and suicidal tendencies. Around 15–20% of the world population is affected by this condition. Major depressive disorder is multifactorial in nature and is related to disturbances in hypothalamus-pituitary-adrenal axis, reduced neurogenesis, inflammation, oxidative stress etc. As Curcumin is effective against all these conditions, it was an obvious choice for performing the clinical study on the patients suffering from major depressive disorder.

Investigation of the Efficacy of Adjunctive Therapy with Bioavailability-Boosted Curcuminoids in Major Depressive Disorder

## Investigation of the efficacy of adjunctive therapy with bioavailability-boosted curcuminoids in major depressive disorder

Panahi *et al.*

*Phytother Res.* 2015c

Researchers at Baqiyatallah University of Medical Sciences, Tehran, Iran performed an open-label trial with the Curcumin C3 Complex® and BioPerine® combination for the management of major depressive disorder. Hundred and eleven subjects diagnosed with major depressive disorder were selected and divided in two groups to receive the standard antidepressant therapy plus the Curcuminoids (Curcumin C3 Complex® 500mg + BioPerine® 5mg) twice a day or just the standard antidepressant therapy for 6 weeks. The efficacy was measured based on the changes in the psychological status Hospital Anxiety and Depression Scale (HADS) and Beck Depression Inventory II (BDI-II). The BDI-II is a widely cited self reporting scale for evaluating presence and severity of depression, and comprises of subscales, which assess both somatic and cognitive symptoms. One-hundred and seven subjects completed the 6-week trial and results showed that HADS score was significantly reduced in the Curcuminoids group as well as in control group. However, the decrease was more in the Curcuminoids group, which shows the benefits of Curcuminoids in the management of major depressive disorder. Similarly, the BDI-II self reported scores showed reduction in both the groups but the decrease was more in the Curcuminoids group, which showed the benefits of Curcuminoids over the standard therapy. The present study showed that use of Curcuminoids combination (Curcumin C3 Complex® and BioPerine®) is well tolerated and safe for long term use, and can help in the management of major depressive disorder [Panahi *et al.* 2015c].

# Obesity

Obesity is one of the major health worries in the modern world caused by excessive food intake, loss of physical activities, genetic susceptibility and sometimes due to endocrinal disorder. Obesity is also considered as a major risk factor for development of many other diseases like hyperlipidemia, hypertension, osteoarthritis, diabetes, atherosclerosis and increased cardiovascular risk. It has reached to epidemic levels in countries like the US, where over 33% adult population suffers from obesity. Management of lipid levels in obese subjects is of great interest for the management of obesity and related health conditions. Since oxidative stress and inflammation are closely linked with the risk factors associated with the hyperlipidemic conditions, Curcuminoids, well known antioxidant and anti-inflammatory agents have also been considered as natural alternatives for the management of lipid levels. Animal studies have shown that Curcumin can lower the lipid levels by reducing the total cholesterol as well as lipid peroxidation levels, however, the clinical studies have been a few and not on obese subjects. Curcumin C3 Complex® and BioPerine® combination was chosen as the Curcuminoids of choice to study the effects on lipid levels by the researchers at Mashhad University of Medical Sciences, Mashhad, Iran.

Effects of Supplementation with Curcuminoids on Dyslipidemia in Obese Patients: A Randomized Crossover Trial

# Effects of supplementation with curcuminoids on dyslipidemia in obese patients: a randomized crossover trial

Mohammadi *et al.*

*Phytother Res.* 2013

Researchers at Mashhad University of Medical Sciences, Mashhad, Iran conducted a randomized, double-blind, placebo-controlled, cross-over trial with 30 obese subjects. These subjects were not taking lipid-lowering agents at the time of the clinical trial. The subjects were randomized to receive Curcuminoids-Piperine combination (1000 mg-10 mg/day) or placebo for 30 days. After a wash out period of two weeks, subjects were crossed over to other regimen for an alternative treatment for next 30 days. Blood samples were drawn from each subject before and after each treatment period. The lipid levels such as low density lipoprotein (LDL)-cholesterol, high density lipoprotein (HDL)-cholesterol, total cholesterol and triglyceride levels were measured. Results of the clinical study showed that Curcumin C3 Complex® and BioPerine® combination was safe and was well tolerated in obese subjects. Curcumin supplementation also showed a significant lowering down of triglyceride levels in the subjects (Fig. 21). One of the strong points of this clinical trial was its cross-over design, because each subject served as his own control and thus, eliminated the inter-individual differences. Researchers hypothesized that the antihypertriglyceridemic activity of Curcumin may be due to its insulin sensitization effects [Mohammadi *et al.* 2013].

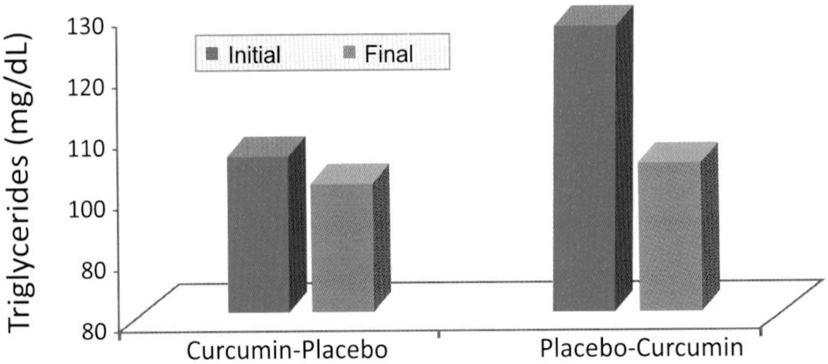


**Fig. 21:** Effect of Curcumin supplementation on serum triglyceride levels

# *Effect of Curcumin on Total Cholesterol*

Obesity is also recognized as a state of chronic oxidative stress and inflammation. State of oxidative stress may trigger the protective mechanism in the body through expression of heat shock proteins such as Hsp-27. The induction of heat shock protein can elicit cytokine production or modulate the immune response. However, their chronic over expression can have adverse effect and is involved in the pathogenesis of several diseases including atherosclerosis. This study was conducted to assess the effects of Curcumin on oxidative stress and levels of Hsp-27 by using rapid assay of pro-oxidant–antioxidant balance.

Curcuminoids Modulate Pro-Oxidant–Antioxidant Balance but not the Immune Response to Heat Shock Protein 27 and Oxidized LDL in Obese Individuals

## Curcuminoids modulate pro-oxidant-antioxidant balance but not the immune response to heat shock protein 27 and oxidized LDL in obese individuals

Sahebkar *et al.*

*Phytother Res.* 2013

Researchers at Mashhad University of Medical Sciences, Mashhad, Iran conducted a double-blind, randomized, placebo-controlled, two-arm, two-period, cross-over, 30 days clinical trial on 30 subjects, which were included in the study based on the following criteria (Table 1):

**Table 1**: Inclusion criteria for the study subjects.

| Criteria | Clinical Condition(s) | Risk Factor(s) | Limit |
|---|---|---|---|
| I | Coronary Heart Disease | < 2 | 160 mg/dL < LDL-C< 190 mg/dL |
| II | BMI | -- | $\geq$ 30 kg/m$^2$ |
| III | Coronary Heart Disease | $\geq$ 2 | 130 mg/dL < LDL-C < 160 mg/dL |

BMI: Body-mass Index
LDL-C: Low Density Lipoprotein-Cholesterol

Subjects were divided as active and placebo groups and administered either 1 g/day Curcuminoids (Curcumin C3 Complex®-1000 mg and BioPerine®-10 mg) or matching placebo. After 30 days of treatment the subjects were crossed over with 2-week washout period. Blood samples were collected at baseline and at the end of each treatment period. Since the study was cross-over design, each subject acted as their own control and eliminated the individual variations. Serum anti-Hsp-27 assay, Serum anti-oxLDL assay (Serum antibody titre to oxidized low density lipoprotein measured by a sandwich ELISA technique) and modified pro-oxidant–antioxidant balance (PAB) assays were performed. The results indicated that Curcuminoids supplementation significantly reduced the serum pro-oxidant–antioxidant balance levels without affecting the anti-Hsp-27 and anti-oxLDL levels (Fig. 22). Pro-oxidant–antioxidant balance test can be regarded as an index of oxidative stress and its reduction in the current clinical study with supplementation of Curcuminoids implies the antioxidant and cardioprotective role of Curcuminoids. The absence of correlation in levels of heat shock proteins and pro-oxidant–antioxidant balance levels can imply that Curcumin may be modulating the cardiovascular risk through a mechanism other than blocking the immune response towards the heat shock proteins (Hsp), whereas at the same time providing the antioxidant support and mitigating oxidative stress. Researchers concluded that Curcuminoids-Piperine supplementation of 1000 mg-10 mg/day for 30 days resulted in a significant reduction of serum pro-oxidant–antioxidant balance and cardiovascular risk [Sahebkar *et al.* 2013].

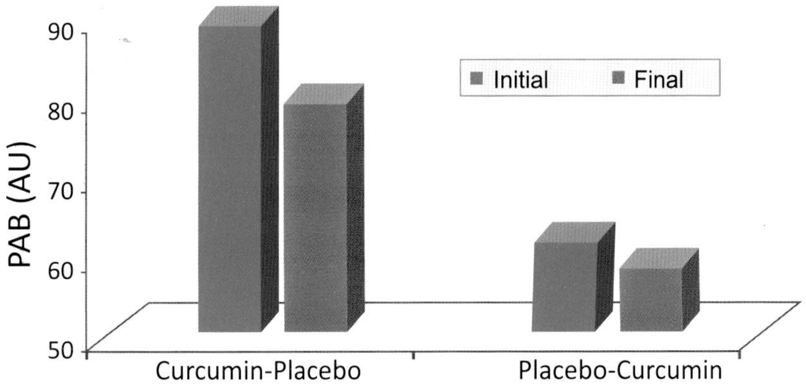


**Fig. 22:** Effect of Curcumin supplementation on Pro-oxidant Antioxidant Balance (PAB)

The previous two clinical trials [Mohammadi *et al.* 2012 and Sahebkar *et al.* 2013] were performed to evaluate the benefits of Curcuminoids in modulating the lipid levels and oxidative stress in obese subjects with hyperlipidemic conditions. Taking this forward, anti-inflammatory effects of Curcuminoids were also assessed in obese subjects.

Clinical Study
Investigation of the Effects of Curcumin on Serum Cytokines in Obese Individuals: A Randomized Controlled Trial

# Investigation of the effects of curcumin on serum cytokines in obese individuals: a randomized controlled trial

Ganjali *et al.*

*The Scientific World Journal* 2014

As obesity is associated with strong inflammatory response and is often accompanied by increased levels of pro-inflammatory cytokines and impaired antioxidant status, the present study was performed on the frozen serum samples collected from subjects during the previous trial to understand the effect of Curcumin's anti-inflammatory role in the hyperlipidemic conditions in obese subjects. The results indicated that Curcumin was able to modulate the inflammatory response in obese subjects. Evaluation of serum samples from obese subjects indicated that serum concentrations of interleukin-1β, vascular endothelial growth factor and interleukin-4 were significantly reduced following Curcumin C3 Complex®-BioPerine® supplementation (Fig. 23). In the previous study [Sahebkar *et al.* 2013], researchers observed that Curcuminoids supplementation resulted in the reduction of pro-oxidant–antioxidant balance index indicating the inhibition of oxidative stress and it further validated the previous results. This study is the first cross-over study on the anti-inflammatory activity of Curcumin in obese subjects [Ganjali *et al.* 2014].

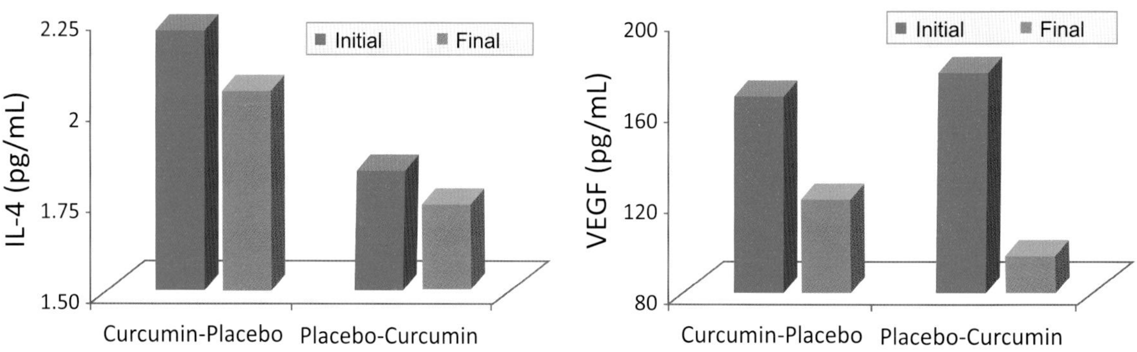


**Fig. 23:** Effect of Curcuminoids on serum cytokine parameters

An Investigation of the Effects of Curcumin on Anxiety and Depression in Obese Individuals: A Randomized Controlled Trial

# An investigation of the effects of curcumin on anxiety and depression in obese individuals: A randomized controlled trial

Esmaily *et al.*

*Chin J Integr Med*. 2015

A study was published in 2006 on relationship between obesity and range of mood disorders, and anxiety. In the US population, it was observed that obesity was associated with approximately 25% increase in odds of mood disorders and anxiety disorders (Simon *et al*. 2006). Today, we recognize the vicious circle of obesity, which is more prevalent in patients suffering from anxiety and depression. Inflammation and oxidative stress are regarded as key factors in pathogenesis of neurotoxicity and inflammation. Disruption of hypothalamic-pituitary-adrenal axis is one of the distinct features of anxiety and depression. Thus, a battery of these factors - imbalance in hypothalamic-pituitary-adrenal axis and heightened inflammation along with lifestyle alterations is thought to be responsible for obesity.

In a 4-week, randomized, double-blind, cross-over clinical trial, researchers at Mashhad University of Medical Sciences, Mashhad, Iran evaluated the impact of Curcumin supplementation on depression and anxiety indices in 30 obese subjects. Subjects were administered either 1 g/day dosage of Curcumin C3 Complex® and 10 mg of BioPerine® in 2 equally divided dosages or matching placebo. After completion of dose regimen of 30 days, the patients were crossed over after 2 weeks of washout period. Beck Anxiety Inventory (BAI) and Beck Depression Inventory (BDI) scales were filled out for each participant at baseline and after 4, 6 and 10 weeks of trial initiation.

Results from the trial showed a significant reduction in the mean Beck Anxiety Inventory score in the active group subjects as compared to placebo group. Authors of the study suggested that Curcuminoids supplementation for 4 weeks in obese subjects was able to show significant antianxiety effect. Authors also explained that bioavailability issue of Curcuminoids supplementation was overcome by addition of BioPerine® as a bioavailability enhancer. It was suggested that the current study was able to provide highest level of evidence due to its cross-over design [Esmaily *et al.* 2015].

# Metabolic Syndrome

Before we could understand the meaning and significance of the term metabolic syndrome (Met S), it already has taken epidemic proportions. Metabolic syndrome is a serious health problem affecting millions around the world today in both developed and underdeveloped countries, one third of the US population is suffering from metabolic syndrome. It is diagnosed as simultaneous occurrence of several risk factors such as hypertension, hyperglycemia, abdominal obesity and atherogenic dyslipidemia. Building up of these risk factors increases the risk of coronary heart disease (CHD) and type-2 diabetes in patients. Atherogenic dyslipidemia, one of the main features of metabolic syndrome has been associated with increase in plasma triglyceride levels and low high density lipoprotein-cholesterol levels.

The key to management of metabolic syndrome is controlling individual risk factors and the most prominent and modifiable factor is dyslipidemia. Since there are cluster of risk factors working in tandem, benefits of drugs such as statins used for the management of dyslipidemia are limited. Many of the risk factors of metabolic syndrome have been shown related to oxidative stress by recent researchers. In some published experimental and clinical studies, metabolic syndrome patients have been shown to have over production of reactive oxygen species, diminution in antioxidant enzymes, increase in lipid peroxidation and protein oxidation biomarkers. Hence, there is a need to find safe and effective products for the management of risk factors of metabolic syndrome. Curcumin with its potential to modulate the risk factors of metabolic syndrome was an obvious choice. The following constellation of studies show that Curcumin being versatile in its activity against inflammation, oxidative stress, hypertension and hyperglycemia can be an useful tool in the management of metabolic syndrome, and also in conditions such as insulin resistance, which is a core factor in the development of metabolic syndrome and hepatic steatosis, which is regarded as hepatic manifestation of metabolic syndrome.

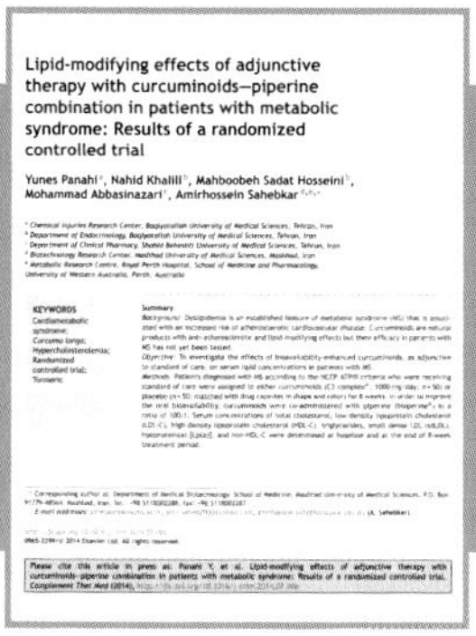
Lipid-modifying effects of adjunctive therapy with curcuminoids–piperine combination in patients with metabolic syndrome: Results of a randomized controlled trial

Yunes Panahi[a], Nahid Khalili[b], Mahboobeh Sadat Hosseini[b], Mohammad Abbasinazari[c], Amirhossein Sahebkar[d,e,*]

[a] Chemical Injuries Research Center, Baqiyatallah University of Medical Sciences, Tehran, Iran
[b] Department of Endocrinology, Baqiyatallah University of Medical Sciences, Tehran, Iran
[c] Department of Clinical Pharmacy, Shahid Beheshti University of Medical Sciences, Tehran, Iran
[d] Biotechnology Research Center, Mashhad University of Medical Sciences, Mashhad, Iran
[e] Metabolic Research Centre, Royal Perth Hospital, School of Medicine and Pharmacology, University of Western Australia, Perth, Australia

KEYWORDS
Cardiometabolic syndrome;
Curcuma longa;
Hypercholesterolemia;
Randomized controlled trial;
Turmeric

Summary

Please cite this article in press as: Panahi Y, et al. Lipid-modifying effects of adjunctive therapy with curcuminoids–piperine combination in patients with metabolic syndrome: Results of a randomized controlled trial. Complement Ther Med (2014)

## Lipid modifying effects of adjunctive therapy with curcuminoids-piperine combination in patients with metabolic syndrome: results of a randomized controlled trial

Panahi *et al.*

*Complement Ther Med.* 2014c

In a randomized, double-blind, placebo-controlled, parallel-group clinical study conducted by researchers at Baqiyatallah University of Medical Sciences, Tehran, Iran, for evaluating the benefits of Curcumin's lipid modifying activity, 100 patients with metabolic syndrome (according to NCEP-ATPIII criteria) were enrolled and randomized either to receive Curcuminoids-Piperine combination (1000 mg-10 mg/day) or matching placebo for 8 weeks. Subjects included in the clinical trial fulfilled the following diagnostic criteria as summarized in Table 2.

**Table** 2: Diagnostic criteria for subjects included in the trial.

| S. No. | Diagnostic Criteria | Values |
|---|---|---|
| 1 | Waist Circumference | > 102 cm (Male)<br>> 88 cm (Female) |
| 2 | Blood Pressure | > 130/85 mm Hg |
| 3 | Triglycerides* | > 150.57 mg/dL |
| 4 | HDL-C* | < 39.82 mg/dL (Male)<br>< 49.88 mg/dL (Female) |
| 5 | Fasting Glucose Levels* | > 109.8 mg/dL |

HDL-C: High-density lipoprotein-Cholesterol
*Converted values

The subjects were already receiving standard care for metabolic syndrome, which included lipid-lowering agents. Fasting blood samples were collected at baseline and at the end of the trial. The use of Curcuminoids-Piperine combination was found to be safe and very well tolerated in subjects with metabolic syndrome. Supplementation with Curcumin C3 Complex®-BioPerine® combination resulted in greater reduction of serum triglycerides, total cholesterol, serum low density lipoprotein-cholesterol, non-high density lipoprotein-cholesterol, Lipoprotein(a) [Lp(a)] and increase in high density lipoprotein-cholesterol concentrations as compared to placebo group. Overall, authors of the study concluded Curcumin C3 Complex®-BioPerine® combination as a safe and effective adjuvant for controlling influence on lipid profile of subjects with metabolic syndrome on standard treatment [Panahi *et al.* 2014c].

Clinical Nutrition

Antioxidant and anti-inflammatory effects of curcuminoid-piperine combination in subjects with metabolic syndrome: A randomized controlled trial and an updated meta-analysis

## Antioxidant and anti-inflammatory effects of curcuminoid-piperine combination in subjects with metabolic syndrome: A randomized controlled trial and an updated meta-analysis

Panahi *et al.*

*Clin Nutr*. 2015d

Following the previous trial [Panahi *et al.* 2014c], which showed the improvement in lipid levels in patients using Curcumin C3 Complex®-BioPerine® combination as an adjuvant in the management of metabolic syndrome, another clinical trial was planned. This Phase III, randomized, double-blind, placebo-controlled trial was conducted at Baqiyatallah University of Medical Sciences, Tehran, Iran with 117 subjects diagnosed with metabolic syndrome (according to NCEP-ATPIII criteria) as mentioned in the previous clinical trial. The inclusion criteria for this clinical trial included that subjects prior to enrolling in the trial were not receiving lipid lowering therapy. Subjects were randomized into two groups: active and placebo. The active group received Curcuminoids-Piperine combination (1000 mg-10 mg/day) for 8 weeks. Fasting blood samples were withdrawn from all subjects at baseline and at the end of the trial. Authors of the study also conducted a meta-analysis for

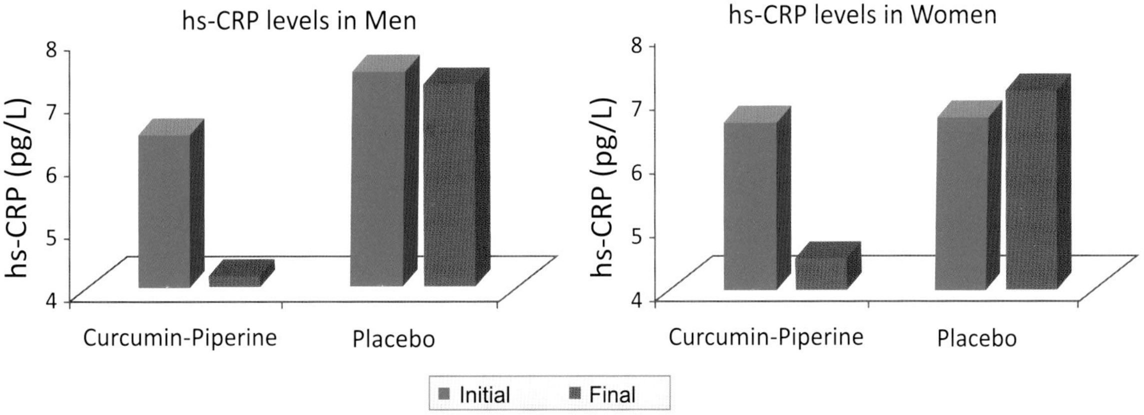


**Fig. 24:** Reduction in serum hs-CRP levels: Curcumin-Piperine vs. Placebo in both men and women

estimating the effects of Curcuminoid therapy on serum C-reactive protein (CRP) concentrations considering it as a risk factor for cardiovascular disease. Results of the meta-analysis showed that Curcuminoids supplementation significantly reduced the serum hs-CRP concentrations (Fig. 24). Further, Curcuminoids-Piperine combination improved the biomarkers of inflammation and oxidative stress. Results of the study showed reduced serum malondialdehyde and C-reactive protein concentration and higher serum superoxide dismutase activity. Based on the results, it was suggested Curcumin C3 Complex®-BioPerine® as an effective natural supplement for managing metabolic syndrome [Panahi *et al.* 2015d].

# Cardiovascular Disorders

Among various organs in our body, heart is the most efficient. A number of physiological changes happen due to which cardiac health gets affected either directly or indirectly. The basic reason would be "fat metabolism", which is the key factor for almost all the complications like heart attack, artery blockage, blood pressure etc. The reason why it is important is because the composition of good fats (high density lipoproteins), bad fats (low density lipoproteins) and essential fats need to be maintained. The normal fat/lipoprotein metabolism is reversed in other ways, which leads to increase in low density lipoproteins and decrease in high density lipoproteins, which are vice versa in normal lipoprotein metabolism. Inflammation is crucially involved in different stages of artherosclerosis, namely serum concentrations of C-reactive protein. Curcumin, known for its anti-inflammatory potential has been evaluated for its role in cardiovascular disorder in the following study.

**The Effect of Curcumin on some of Traditional and Non-traditional Cardiovascular Risk Factors: A Pilot Randomized, Double-blind, Placebo-controlled Trial**

Parastoo Mirzabeigi, Amir Hooshang Mohammadpour, Mojtaba Salarifar, Khairollah Gholami, Mojtaba Mojtahedzadeh and Mohammad Reza Javadi

Abstract

Keywords: Curcumin; Coronary artery disease; Lipid profile; hs-CRP; Blood glucose

Introduction

Cardiovascular diseases (CVDs) and their complications are considered as a leading cause of death throughout the world. They can also decrease quality of life. Traditional risk factors of cardiovascular diseases include age, gender, hypertension, dyslipidemia, smoking and diabetes mellitus (1). Among these, dyslipidemia is the atheromatous lesion's foundation, which accompanied with arterial stenosis. Although these risk factors have a strong association with cardiovascular events, they are insufficient to fully elucidate absolute risk. Therefore the probability of interference of other factors in the pathogenesis of atherosclerosis is considerable (2). Numerous studies have pointed to crucial position of inflammation throughout atherosclerosis stages (3, 4). Studies stated

# The Effect of Curcumin on some of Traditional and Non-traditional Cardiovascular Risk Factors: A Pilot Randomized, Double-blind, Placebo-controlled Trial

Mirzabeigi *et al.*

*Iran J Pharm Res.* 2015

In a randomized study on 33 patients suffering from coronary artery disease (CAD), 500 mg capsule of Curcumin C3 Complex® was given four times a day for 8 weeks. Parameters evaluated at baseline and at the end of the study included lipid profile, blood glucose and hs-CRP. A significant improvement was observed in individuals taking Curcumin in comparison to baseline values, wherein a reduction in serum values of triglycerides, low density lipoprotein (Fig. 25) and very-low density lipoprotein were recorded [Mirzabeigi *et al.* 2015]. This has paved way for further extensive studies on the use of Curcuminoids in cardiovascular disorders.

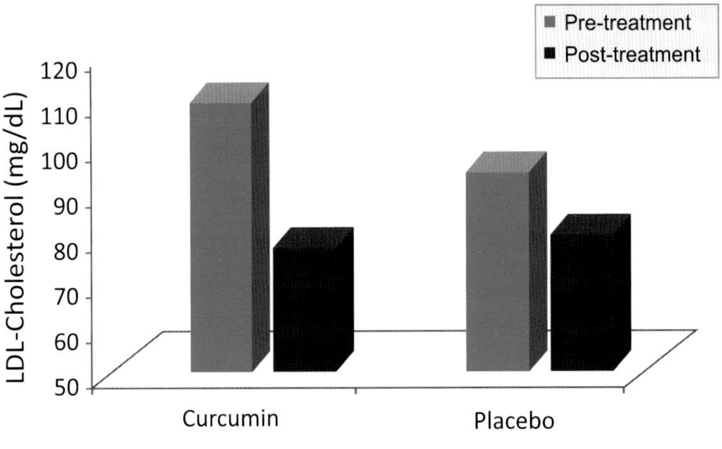


**Fig. 25:** The effect of Curcumin on cardiovascular risk factors

 

# Bioavailability

Curcumin possesses tremendous potential to benefit human health, however, its rapid biotransformation has often been cited as a reason for its limited bioavailability. The fact that Curcumin undergoes rapid biotransformation in the gut and liver lead to speculation regarding the bioavailability of Curcumin and also about its metabolic fate. As the research on Curcumin progressed with time, today we have a better insight of Curcumin's metabolism in the body.

Curcumin is metabolized by both conjugation and reduction pathways in the body resulting in formation of several metabolites as shown in the following Fig. 26.

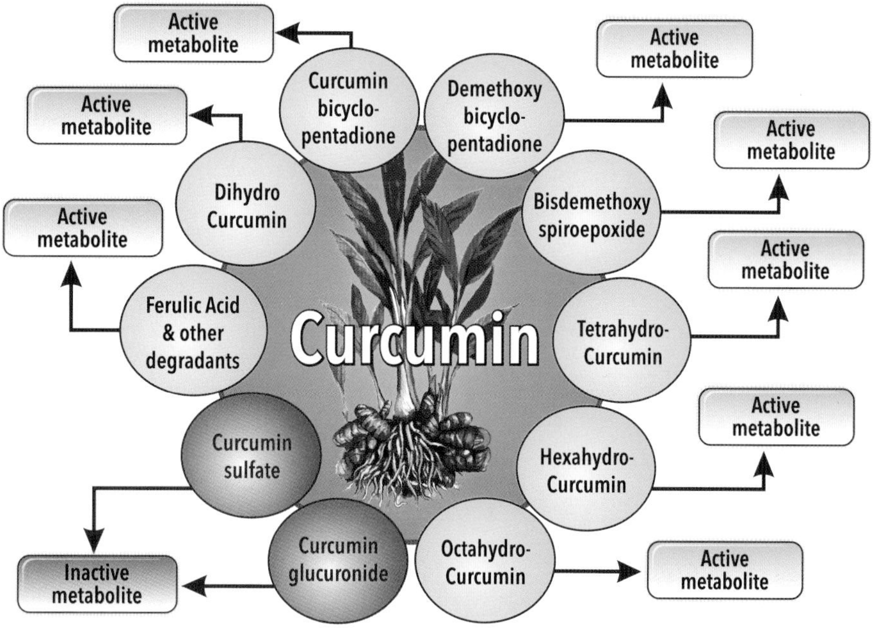


**Fig. 26:** Metabolism of Curcumin

Recent studies have shown that conjugates such as glucuronides and sulphates are pharmacologically inactive. Some studies on the reduced metabolites such as Tetrahydrocurcuminoids have provided very interesting comparison with Curcuminoids in biological activity. Number of studies have reported the antioxidant, anti–inflammatory, antidiabetic, antihyperlipidemic, antiglycation, neuroprotective and hepatoprotective activities for Tetrahydrocurcuminoids. Further, these active metabolites of Curcumin caught a lot of interest in 2011, when Proceeding of National Academy of Sciences (PNAS) published a path breaking report on how Curcumin was able to generate Tetrahydrocurcuminoids by undergoing enzymatic reduction through an enzyme CurA, present in commensal gut microbes *E. coli* [Hassaninasab *et al.* 2011].

Thus, the metabolic fate of Curcumin leads to both active and inactive metabolites. In order to improve the biological activity of Curcumin, biotransformation of Curcumin into its inactive metabolites need to be inhibited, freeing the substrate for conversion into active metabolites. Scientists at Sabinsa discovered the natural solution for the above challenge in the form of BioPerine®, an extract obtained from black pepper fruits, a patented product of Sabinsa.

Sabinsa evaluated the bioavailability of Curcumin C3 Complex® in presence of BioPerine® through both animal and human studies. BioPerine® is obtained from black pepper fruits (*Piper nigrum*) extract and bio-standardized to 95% piperine. Piperine is also well known for its thermogenic activity and is an inhibitor of hepatic and intestinal glucuronidation.

Influence of Piperine on the Pharmacokinetics of Curcumin in Animals and Human Volunteers

# Influence of piperine on the pharmacokinetics of Curcumin in animals and human volunteers

Shoba *et al.*

*Planta Med.* 1998

This randomized, cross-over clinical study was carried out at St. John's Medical College, Bangalore, India to assess the potential of BioPerine® for increasing the bioavailability of Curcuminoids. An animal study on rats preceded the clinical study. The results from the animal study clearly showed the presence of Curcuminoids in higher concentration in the serum in presence of BioPerine® at 1 h and 2 h of administration of Curcumin and BioPerine®. The results were encouraging for performing the clinical trial for this combination (Fig. 27).

Ten healthy volunteers aged between 20-26 years were enrolled for the clinical study. The subjects were administered 2 g Curcumin followed by two weeks of washout period and crossed over to receive 2 g of Curcumin and BioPerine® (20 mg) combination. The blood samples were taken at 0.25, 0.5, 0.75, 1, 2, 3, 4, 5 and 6 h post administration on each occasion. Both Curcumin and Curcumin-piperine combination were well tolerated by the subjects with no adverse events.

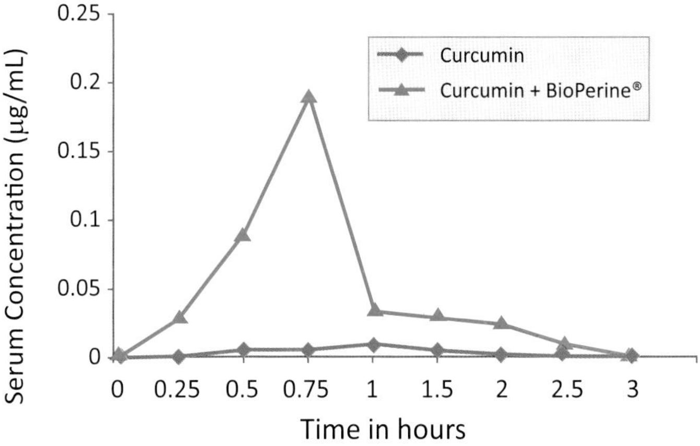


**Fig. 27:** Serum concentration µg/ml (mean ± SEM) of Curcumin 2 g oral alone and with piperine 20 mg in humans (n=8)

The plasma samples collected from subjects were estimated for Curcumin content by HPLC. The results obtained from the clinical trial were in accordance with animal model study carried out earlier. The results from the human trial demonstrated that piperine can enhance the oral bioavailability of Curcumin with Curcumin serum concentration peaking at 1 h and relative bioavailability of Curcumin was found to be increased by 2000% or 20 folds by piperine.

This study was a path-breaking and first of its kind to demonstrate the bio-enhancing potential of piperine in BioPerine®. This study evidenced that piperine is a potent inhibitor for metabolism of certain nutrients/dietary ingredients, which can alter the rate of glucuronidation in gut and liver, thus slowing down the transformation and increasing bioavailability of the nutrients [Shoba *et al*. 1998].

The study published on the above clinical trial is one of the most downloaded papers of *Planta Medica* journal.

While human bioavailability study on the BioPerine® combination with Curcumin showed potential of increasing bioavailability of Curcumin, its need for enhancing the therapeutic potential of Curcumin in health compromised subjects was realized after a clinical study conducted by University of Leicester, UK [Garcea *et al*. 2004].

Detection of curcumin and its metabolites in hepatic tissue and portal blood of patients following oral administration

# Detection of curcumin and its metabolites in hepatic tissue and portal blood of patients following oral administration

Garcea *et al.*

*Br J Cancer*. 2004

Researchers at Leicester University, UK performed a clinical trial on 12 patients with hepatic metastatic disease from primary colorectal adenocarcinoma. The patients received Curcumin C3 Complex® in capsules with dose levels of 1, 4 or 8 capsules daily (equivalent to 450 mg, 1800 mg or 3600 mg of Curcuminoids) daily for 1-week prior to the surgery. Purpose of the clinical study was to evaluate if the oral administration of Curcumin can reach to effective amounts of Curcumin in normal and malignant liver tissue after passing through the gut.

Results showed that in patients suffering from hepatic metastases, the uptake of Curcumin was poor and did not reach to therapeutic levels. Therefore, it was concluded that the poor bioavailability can affect the feasibility of its role as a therapeutic agent in chemotherapy-induced apoptosis in tissues remote from the gastrointestinal (GI) tract [Garcea *et al.* 2004].

This prompted researchers to relook at the means to improve the bioavailability of Curcumin in the body. Hence, Curcumin C3 Complex® and BioPerine® combination, which was used in many clinical studies later on to improve the bioavailability of Curcumin in tissues remote to the GI tract.

While researchers continued to use the Curcuminoids and BioPerine® combination, studies are being carried out to evaluate the efficacy of this combination in various health conditions including Alzheimer's, cognitive support, several types of premalignant and malignant cancers. It also promoted a need to understand the safety of commercially available Curcumin-BioPerine® combination. Since piperine can affect several pathways such as

CYP3A, CYP2C9, UGT and SULT, it was deemed necessary to evaluate if this combination can affect the pharmacokinetic disposition of any of the drugs working through above mentioned pathways.

With this, the following study was taken up with the primary objective of assessing the safety of this combination when taken along with drugs such as Midazolam, Flurbiprofen or Paracetamol, which work through the above mentioned pathways.

BJCP British Journal of Clinical Pharmacology

Effect of a herbal extract containing curcumin and piperine on midazolam, flurbiprofen and paracetamol (acetaminophen) pharmacokinetics in healthy volunteers

## Effect of a herbal extract containing Curcumin and piperine on midazolam, flurbiprofen and paracetamol (acetaminophen) pharmacokinetics in healthy volunteers

Volak *et al.*

*Br J Clin Pharmacol*. 2013

Researchers at Tuft University School of Medicine, Boston, USA conducted a randomized, placebo-controlled, six-way, cross-over study on eight healthy subjects to assess the safety of short-term use of Curcumin-BioPerine® combination with concurrent intake of drugs metabolized by CYP3A, CYP2C9 , SULT and UGT pathways. In this study, combination of Curcumin C3 Complex®-BioPerine® (at a dosage of 500 mg of Curcumin C3 Complex® and 3 mg of BioPerine®) or matching placebo was given orally four times over 2 days before oral administration of midazolam, flurbiprofen or paracetamol. Plasma and urine concentrations of drugs, metabolites and Curcumin C3 Complex®-BioPerine® at different time points were measured by HPLC.

The results from the clinical study showed that there was no clinically significant effect of the Curcumin - Piperine combination on the pharmacokinetics disposition of probe drugs as compared to placebo. Thus, the current finding showed that Curcumin-Piperine combination does not have the ability to modify the substantial disposition of medications, which are dependent on CYP3A, CYP2C9, UGT and SULT pathways, thus proving the safety of Curcumin C3 Complex® and BioPerine® combination [Volak *et al.* 2013].

# Oxidative Stress – A Meta-analysis

Oxidative stress is now considered as a precursor of many human disorders and health conditions. Oxidative stress is defined as the disturbance in balance between production of reactive oxygen species and the inability of the body's defense system to neutralize them. Oxidative stress can be induced by a number of factors including intrinsic and extrinsic. Free radicals are commonly formed in the body as an outcome of aerobic cellular metabolism as well introduced in the body from environment, food, toxins etc. One such reactive oxygen intermediate is superoxide anion, which may produce related toxic products in the body. Superoxide dismutase can convert superoxide into hydrogen peroxide, which is later converted into water by catalysis and glutathione peroxidase. However, over production of the super oxide in the body can lead to oxidative stress. The chronic over production of free radicals can promote disease conditions, even leading to cancer due to oxidative damage to DNA.

As Curcumin's principal role in the body is related to its antioxidant activity, researchers from 4 different Universities performed a meta-analysis to assess the impact of Curcuminoids supplementation on plasma activities of superoxide dismutase, catalase, glutathione and lipid peroxides as parameters of oxidative stress. Meta–analysis is a powerful tool, which helps in assessing the clinical effectiveness of an intervention by combining the results of two or more randomized clinical trials using statistical tools.

**Effect of curcuminoids on oxidative stress: A systematic review and meta-analysis of randomized controlled trials**

Amirhossein Sahebkar, Maria-Corina Serban, Sorin Ursoniu, Maciej Banach

ARTICLE INFO

ABSTRACT

1. Introduction

# Effect of curcuminoids on oxidative stress: A systematic review and meta-analysis of randomized controlled trials

Sahebkar *et al.*

*J Funct Foods*. 2015

Researchers at Mashhad University (Iran), University of Western Australia (Perth), University of Medicine and Pharmacy, Timisoara (Romania) and Medical University of Lodz (Poland) performed a meta-analysis on Curcumin formulations to assess the effect of Curcuminoids supplementation on oxidative stress in health as well as in disease conditions.

The meta-analysis was based on the guidelines of Preferred Reporting Items for Systematic Reviews and Meta-analysis (PRISMA) statement, 2009. The data was searched using PUBMED, Cochrane Library, Scopus and EMBACE databases. The search was limited to randomized-controlled human trials done from January 1, 1970 to September 1, 2014. Inclusion criteria for the studies were; randomized-controlled trials (RCTs) with parallel or cross-over design, investigation of serum/plasma superoxide dismutase activities and sufficient information on serum superoxide dismutase activities at the beginning and at the end of the study for control and active groups. The data was extracted and quality of studies, which were included in this meta-analysis was done using Jadad scale. Meta-analysis was done by Review Manager version 5.2 (Cochrane collaboration) and Comprehensive Meta-Analysis (CMA) V2 software (Biostat, NJ). All information related to serum activities of superoxide dismutase, catalase, concentration of lipid peroxides and glutathione were collected for calculating standard deviation and mean difference. Sensitivity analysis was done to estimate the overall effect size of individual studies [Sahebkar *et al.* 2015].

## Results:

Six studies were selected, in total 396 subjects were randomized out of which 197 subjects received Curcumin supplementation in dose range of 80-1500 mg/day for 4-8 weeks.

- All the studies selected in this meta-analysis showed that Curcumin supplementation was safe and very well tolerated by the subjects with no serious adverse events
- The data received from meta-analysis of the 6 randomized-controlled trials showed that Curcumin supplementation was significantly able to increase serum superoxide dismutase activities. Sensitivity analysis showed that effect size was robust for individual studies

## Conclusion:

Results of the meta-analysis showed that Curcumin supplementation was able to significantly affect all the parameters of oxidative stress. There was a significant increase in serum activities of superoxide dismutase and catalase, serum glutathione concentration and decrease in serum lipid peroxides. The meta-analysis results indicated that Curcumin supplementation was able to alleviate the symptoms of oxidative stress, thus this phytochemical may be useful in treating ailments for which oxidative stress is involved in pathogenesis.

# C-Reactive Protein Lowering Effect-A Meta-analysis

Inflammation is now recognized as the root cause of several chronic health conditions and diseases. Inflammation manifests itself through increase in several inflammatory proteins and cell signaling molecules in the body. One of the proteins of interest here is C-reactive protein, which is an acute phase reactant. The presence of high C-reactive protein levels is considered as an indication of inflammation in the body. C-reactive proteins as a marker for inflammation is particularly important in the cardiovascular diseases. Levels of C-reactive protein are considered as an independent biomarker for cardiovascular disease. C-reactive proteins have been shown to stimulate the aggregation of low density lipoprotein particles and also stimulate the uptake of low density lipoprotein in macrophages resulting in promoting the formation of foam cells. Foam cells are fat laden macrophages and are indicators of plaque build-up increasing the risk of cardiovascular disease.

In fact, a recent study conducted by researchers at Mashhad University of Medical Sciences, Mashhad, Iran showed a significant reduction in the lipid levels [Mohammadi *et al.* 2012]. Curcumin also showed benefits in reduction of C-reactive protein levels. This reduction in C-reactive protein is an indicator in reducing risk of cardiovascular disease.

Continuing the previous research work on hypolipidemic activity of Curcumin, a meta-analysis was planned by researchers at Mashhad University of Medical Sciences, Mashhad, Iran to evaluate the benefit of Curcumin supplementation on elevated C-reactive protein levels.

REVIEW
Are Curcuminoids Effective C-Reactive Protein-Lowering Agents in Clinical Practice? Evidence from a Meta-Analysis

Amirhossein Sahebkar

INTRODUCTION

# Are curcuminoids effective C-reactive protein-lowering agents in clinical practice? Evidence from a meta analysis

Sahebkar *et al.*

*Phytother Res.* 2014

## Objective:

To perform a meta-analysis of clinical trials for investigating the effect of Curcuminoids supplementation on serum C-reactive protein concentrations.

## Study Design:

This meta-analysis was conducted on guidelines based on PRISMA statement, 2009. MEDLINE and SCOPUS databases were searched and studies which fulfilled the eligibility criteria were selected. The eligibility criteria for the meta-analysis were cross-over design, use of Curcuminoids as monotherapy or as adjunctive therapy, enough data on baseline and end of trial C-reactive protein concentrations, use of purified Curcumin extract and if the study was published in peer-reviewed journals. Data was extracted and quality assessment was done on Jadad scale. Cochrane Program Review Manager Version 5.1 (Cochrane collaboration, Oxford, UK) was used for the meta-analysis [Sahebkar *et al.* 2014].

## Results and Discussion:

- Total 6 studies with 312 subjects were included in this meta-analysis. One hundred and seventy two subjects received Curcuminoids intervention and 170 subjects received placebo for duration of 6 days to 3 months
- Random effect analysis showed that Curcuminoids supplementation resulted in significant lowering of the serum C-reactive protein concentrations
- It was shown by power analysis that population pooled was having 100% power for detecting significant difference in C-reactive protein concentrations between active and placebo groups

## Conclusion:

Results of the meta-analysis suggested Curcuminoids as an effective agent in reducing circulating C-reactive protein levels. The authors of the study explained the importance of bioavailability enhancer (BioPerine®) to get maximal therapeutic benefit from the Curcuminoids.

# Clinical Studies In Progress Using Curcumin C3 Complex®

- Evaluation and comparison of Curcumin - Piperine combination as an adjunct to antioxidant therapy in the management of oral submucous fibrosis - An open label trial - Dr. Meenal Tapan, Bharatiya Vidyapeeth Deemed University, Pune, India
- Efficacy of systemic Curcuminoids in the management of oral lichen planus: A randomized controlled trial - Dr. Deepika Keshari, J. S. S Dental College & Hospital, Mysore, India
- Effect of Curcumin on orocecal transit time and oxidative stress levels in patients with ulcerative colitis - Prof. S. V. Rana, PGIMER, Chandigarh, India
- Effect of Curcumin C3 Complex® on patients with non-fatty acid liver disorder - Dr. Amirhossein, Baqiyatallah Hospital, Tehran, Iran
- Role of Curcumin in patients with metastatic gastroesophegal cancer - Dr. Timothy Cannon / Dr. Svetlana Rassulova, CCRC
- Effect of Curcumin on patients with lymphocytic leukemia - Dr. Gary Deng, Memorial Sloan Kettering Cancer Center
- A phase II study of Curcumin and vitamin D in previously untreated patients with early stage chronic lymphocytic lymphoma (CLL) and small lymphocytic lymphoma (SLL) - Dr. Bagem M William. Case Comprehensive Cancer Center, Cleveland, Ohio, USA

# *Conclusion*

Curcumin, due to its traditional use, lower toxicity and broader therapeutic applications in managing the lifestyle health conditions is getting increasing attention from researchers, formulators and consumers alike. Inflammation being the root cause of many chronic diseases, makes Curcuminoids a potent phytochemical for various ailments. While there are many choices in the market available in the field of supplementation of Curcumin, Curcumin C3 Complex® truly stands apart with more than 80+ peer-reviewed publications including 45 clinical studies, a robust supply chain, dedicated manufacturing facility and quality control of the highest level, which has made Curcumin C3 Complex® a gold standard for the industry. To increase its application of use in food, in 2009 Curcumin C3 Complex® obtained self affirmed GRAS status from an independent panel of toxicologists. Later Sabinsa obtained a "No Comment Letter" from USFDA in 2013, which opened the door to its use in a variety of health foods. Hence, "**Bioprotectant**" action of Curcuminoids in Curcumin C3 Complex® helps in maintaining integrity of the biological system by the virtue of its multiple health benefits, which is evident by the number of clinical trials sponsored by Sabinsa Corporation. This resulted in carving a unique place for Curcumin C3 Complex® as "**The Most Trusted Brand**" in the healthcare industry for over two decades and still counting..!!!

# References


Bassiouny AR, Atteya MA, El-Rashidy FH, Neenaa HM. Curcumin and EGCG Suppress Apurinic/Apyrimidinic Endonuclease 1 and Induce Complete Remission in B-cell Non-Hodgkin's lymphoma Patients. *Funct Food Health Dis.* 2011;1(12):525-44.

Bayet-Robert M, Kwiatkowski F, Leheurteur M, Gachon F, Planchat E, Abrial C, Mouret-Reynier MA, Durando X, Barthomeuf C, Chollet P. Phase I dose escalation trial of docetaxel plus curcumin in patients with advanced and metastatic breast cancer. *Cancer Biol Ther.* 2010;9(1):8-14.

Carroll RE, Benya RV, Turgeon DK, Vareed S, Neuman M, Rodriguez L, Kakarala M, Carpenter PM, McLaren C, Meyskens FL. Jr., Brenner DE. Phase IIa clinical trial of curcumin for the prevention of colorectal neoplasia. *Cancer Prev Res.* 2011;4:354-64.

Chainani-Wu N, Silverman S Jr., Reingold A, Bostrom A, McCulloch C, Lozada-Nur F, Weintraub J. A randomized, placebo controlled, double blind clinical trial of curcuminoids in oral lichen planus. *Phytomedicine.* 2007;14(7-8):437-46.

Chainani-Wu N, Madden E, Lozada-Nur F, Silverman S Jr. High-dose curcuminoids are efficacious in the reduction in symptoms and signs of oral lichen planus. *J Am Acad Dermatol.* 2012a; 66(5):752-60.

Chainani-Wu N, Collins K, Silverman S Jr. Use of curcuminoids in a cohort of patients with oral lichen planus, an autoimmune disease. *Phytomedicine.* 2012b;19(5);418-23.

Cruz-Correa M, Shoskes DA, Sanchez P, Zhao R, Hylind LM, Wexner SD, Giardiello FM. Combination treatment with curcumin and quercetin of adenomas in familial adenomatous polyposis. *Clin Gastroenterol Hepatol.* 2006;4:1035-38.

Dhillon N, Aggarwal BB, Newman RA, Wolff RA, Kunnumakkara AB, Abbruzzese JL, Ng CS, Badmaev V, Kurzrock R. Phase II trial of Curcumin in patients with advanced pancreatic cancer. *Clin Cancer Res.* 2008;14(14):4491-99.

Duggi S, Handral HK, Tulsianand G, Shruthi SD. Turmeric: Nature's Precious Medicine. *Asian J Pharm Clin* Res. 2013;6(3):10-16.

Elad S, Meidan I, Sellam G, Simaan S, Zeevi I, Waldman E, Weintraub M, Revel-Vilk S. Topical curcumin for the prevention of oral mucositis in pediatric patients: case series. *Alternative Therapies Health Med.* 2013;19(3):21-24.

Epelbaum R, Schaffer M, Vizel B, Badmaev V, Bar-Sela G. Curcumin and gemcitabine in patients with advanced pancreatic cancer. *Nutr Cancer.* 2010;62(8):1137-41.


 

Esmaily H, Sahebkar A, Iranshahi M, Ganjali S, Mohammadi A, Ferns G, Ghayour-Mobarhan M. An investigation of the effects of curcumin on anxiety and depression in obese individuals: A randomized controlled trial. *Chin J Integr Med*. 2015;21(5):332-38.

Ganjali S, Sahebkar A, Mahdipour E, Jamialahmadi K, Torabi S, Akhlaghi S, Ferns G, Parizadeh SM, Ghayour-Mobarhan M. Investigation of the effects of curcumin on serum cytokines in obese individuals: a randomized controlled trial. *Sci World J*. 2014. DOI:10.1155/2014/898361

Garcea G, Jones DJ, Singh R, Dennison AR, Farmer PB, Sharma RA, Steward WP, Gescher AJ, Berry DP. Detection of curcumin and its metabolites in hepatic tissue and portal blood of patients following oral administration. *Br J Cancer*. 2004;90:1011-15.

Garcea G, Berry DP, Jones DJ, Singh R, Dennison AR, Farmer PB, Sharma RA, Steward WP, Gescher AJ. Consumption of the putative chemopreventive agent curcumin by cancer patients: assessment of curcumin levels in the colorectum and their pharmacodynamics consequences. *Cancer Epidemiol Biomarkers Prev*. 2005;14:120-25.

Golombick T, Diamond TH, Badmaev V, Manoharan A, Ramakrishna R. The potential role of curcumin in patients with monoclonal gammopathy of undefined significance--its effect on paraproteinemia and the urinary N-telopeptide of type I collagen bone turnover marker. *Clin Cancer Res*. 2009;15(18):5917-22.

Golombick T, Diamond TH, Manoharan A, Ramakrishna R. Monoclonal gammopathy of undetermined significance, smoldering multiple myeloma and curcumin: a randomized, double-blind placebo controlled cross-over 4g study and an open-label 8g extension study. *Am J Hematol*. 2012;87(5):455-60.

Hassaninasab A, Hashimoto Y, Tomita-Yokotani K, Kobayashi M. Discovery of the curcumin metabolic pathway involving a unique enzyme in an intestinal microorganism. *Proc Natl Acad Sci* USA. 2011;108(16):6615-20.

Irving GR, Howells LM, Sale S, Kralj-Hans I, Atkin WS, Clark SK, Britton RG, Jones DJ, Scott EN, Berry DP, Hemingway D, Miller AS, Brown K, Gescher AJ, Steward WP. Prolonged biologically active colonic tissue levels of curcumin achieved after oral administration--aclinical pilot study including assessment of patient acceptability. *Cancer Prev Res*. 2013;6(2):119-28.

Irving GR, Iwuji CO, Morgan B, Berry DP, Steward WP, Thomas A, Brown K, Howells LM. Combining curcumin (C3-complex, Sabinsa) with standard care FOLFOX chemotherapy in patients with inoperable colorectal cancer (CUFOX): study protocol for a randomised control trial. *Trials*. 2015;16:110. DOI:10.1186/s13063-015-0641-1.

James MI, Iwuji C, Irving G, Karmokar A, Higgins JA, Griffin-Teal N, Thomas A, Greaves P, Cai H, Patel SR, Morgan B, Dennison A, Metcalfe M, Garcea G, Lloyd DM, Berry DP, Steward WP, Howells LM, Brown K. Curcumin inhibits cancer stem cell phenotypes in ex vivo models of colorectal liver metastases, and is clinically safe and tolerable in combination with FOLFOX chemotherapy. *Cancer Lett*. 2015;364(2):135-41.

 

Kanai M, Yoshimura K, Asada M, Imaizumi A, Suzuki C, Matsumoto S, Nishimura T, Mori Y, Masui T, Kawaguchi Y, Yanagihara K, Yazumi S, Chiba T, Guha S, Aggarwal BB. A phase I/II study of gemcitabine-based chemotherapy plus Curcumin for patients with Gemcitabine-resistant pancreatic cancer. *Cancer Chemother Pharmacol*. 2011;68(1):157-64.

Kurd SK, Smith N, VanVoorhees A, Troxel AB, Badmaev V, Seykora JT, Gelfand JM. Oral curcumin in the treatment of moderate to severe psoriasis vulgaris: A prospective clinical trial. *J Am Acad Dermatol*. 2008;58(4):625-31.

Krup V, Prakash LH, Harini A. Pharmacological Activities of Turmeric (Curcuma longa linn): A Review. *J Homeo Ayur Med*. 2013;2(4):1-4.

Lao C, Ruffin MT, Normolle D, Heath DD, Murray SI, Bailey JM, Boggs ME, Crowell J, Rock CL, Brenner DE. Dose escalation of a curcuminoid formulation. *BMC Complement Altern Med*. 2006;6:10.

Land BV, Blijlevens NMA, Marteijn J, Timal S, Donnelly JP, de Witte TJM, Rabet LM. Role of curcumin and the inhibition of NF-κB in the onset of chemotherapy-induced mucosal barrier injury. *Leukemia* 2004;18:276-84.

Mirzabeigi P, Mohammadpour AH, Salarifar M, Gholami K, Mojtahedzadeh M, Javadi MR. The Effect of Curcumin on some of Traditional and Non-traditional Cardiovascular Risk Factors: A Pilot Randomized, Double-blind, Placebo-controlled Trial. *Iran J Pharm Res*. 2015;14(2):479-86.

Mohammadi A, Sahebkar A, Iranshahi M, Amini M, Khojasteh R, Ghayour-Mobarhan M, Ferns GA. Effects of supplementation with curcuminoids on dyslipidemia in obese patients: a randomized crossover trial. *Phytother Res*. 2013;27(3):374-79.

Majeed M, Rajendran R, Badmaev V. Bioprotectant composition, method of use and extraction process of curcuminoids.1999; US 5,861,415.

Natarajan S and Majeed M. To assess the efficacy and safety of NILIN® SR tablets in the management of osteoarthritis of knee. *Int J Pharm Life Sci*. 2012;3(2):1413-23.

Nhawkar SV, Mullani AK, Magdum CS, D'Souza JI. Quality standardization and toxicity study of ayurvedic formulation. *Int J Bioassays*. 2014;3(9):3244-53.

Panahi Y, Sahebkar A, Amiri M, Davoudi SM, Beiraghdar F, Hoseininejad SL, Kolivand M. Improvement of sulphur mustard-induced chronic pruritus, quality of life and antioxidant status by curcumin: results of a randomised, double-blind, placebo-controlled trial. *Br J Nutr*. 2012a;108(7):1272-79.

Panahi Y, Sahebkar A, Parvin S, Saadat A. A randomized controlled trial on the anti-inflammatory effects of Curcumin in patients with chronic sulphur mustard-induced cutaneous complications. *Ann Clin Biochem*. 2012b;49:580-88.

Panahi Y, Ghanei M, Bashiri S, Hajihashemi A, Sahebkar A. Short-term Curcuminoid Supplementation for Chronic Pulmonary Complications due to Sulfur Mustard Intoxication: Positive Results of a Randomized Double-blind Placebo-controlled Trial. *Drug Res* (Stuttg), 2014a. DOI: 10.1055/s-0034-1389986.

Panahi Y, Rahimnia AR, Sharafi M, Alishiri G, Saburi A, Sahebkar A. Curcuminoid treatment for knee osteoarthritis: a randomized double-blind placebo-controlled Trial. *Phytother Res.* 2014b;28(11):1625-31.

Panahi Y, Khalili N, Hosseini MS, Abbasinazari M, Sahebkar A. Lipid-modifying effects of adjunctive therapy with curcuminoids–piperine combination in patients with metabolic syndrome: results of a randomized controlled trial. *Complement Ther Med.* 2014c;22(5):851-57.

Panahi Y, Ghanei M, Hajhashemi A, Sahebkar A. Effects of Curcuminoids-Piperine Combination on Systemic Oxidative Stress, Clinical Symptomsand Quality of Life in Subjects with Chronic Pulmonary Complications Due to Sulfur Mustard: A Randomized Controlled Trial. *J Diet Suppl.*, 2015a;19:1-13

Panahi Y, Alishiri GH, Parvin S, Sahebkar A. Mitigation of Systemic Oxidative Stress by Curcuminoids in Osteoarthritis: Results of a Randomized Controlled Trial. *J Diet Suppl.* 2015b. DOI:10.3109/19390311.2015.1008611.

Panahi Y, Badeli R, Karami GR, Sahebkar A. Investigation of the efficacy of adjunctive therapy with bioavailability-boosted curcuminoids in major depressive disorder. *Phytother Res.* 2015c;29(1):17-21.

Panahi Y, Hosseini MS, Khalili N, Naimi E, Majeed M, Sahebkar A. Antioxidant and anti-inflammatory effects of curcuminoid-piperine combination in subjects with metabolic syndrome: A randomized controlled trial and an updated meta-analysis. *Clin Nutr.* 2015d. DOI: 10.1016/j.clnu.2014.12.019.

Rahimnia AR, Panahi Y, Alishiri G, Sharafi M, Sahebkar A. Impact of Supplementation with Curcuminoids on Systemic Inflammation in Patients with Knee Osteoarthritis: Findings from a Randomized Double-Blind Placebo-Controlled Trial. *Drug Res.* 2014. DOI: 10.1055/s-0034-1384536.

Ravindran J, Prasad S, Aggarwal BB. Curcumin and cancer cells: how many ways can curry kill tumor cells selectively? *AAPSJ.* 2009;11(3):495-510.

Ravindran PN, Babu KN, Sivaraman K. Turmeric: The genus Curcuma.CRC Press, Taylor & Francis Group, Boca Raton, FL 2007.

Rezvani M and Ross GA. Modification of radiation-induced acute oral mucositis in the rats. *Int J Radiat Bio*l. 2004;80(2):177-82.

Ringman JM, Frautschy SA, Teng E, Begum AN, Bardens J, Beigi M, Gylys KH, Badmaev V, Heath DD, Apostolova LG, Porter V, Vanek Z, Marshall GA, Hellemann G, Sugar C, Masterman DL, Montine TJ, Cummings JL, Cole GM. Oral curcumin for Alzheimer's disease: tolerability and efficacy in a 24 week randomized, double blind, placebo controlled study. *Alzheimer's Res Ther.* 2012;4:43.

 

Ryan JL, Heckler CE, Ling M, Katz A, Williams JP, Pentland AP, Morrow GR. Curcumin for radiation dermatitis: a randomized, double-blind, placebo-controlled clinical trial of thirty breast cancer patients. *Radiat Res.* 2013;180(1):34-43.

Sahebkar A, Mohammadi A, Atabati A, Rahiman S, Tavallaie S, Iranshahi M, Akhlaghi S, Ferns GA, Ghayour-Mobarhan M. Curcuminoids modulate pro-oxidant antioxidant balance but not the immune response to heat shock protein 27 and oxidized LDL in obese individuals. *Phytother Res.* 2013;27(12):1883-88.

Sahebkar A. Are curcuminoids effective C-reactive protein-lowering agents in clinical practice? Evidence from a meta-analysis. *Phytother Res.* 2014;28:633-42.

Sahebkar A, Serban M, Ursoniu S, Banach M. Effect of curcuminoids on oxidative stress: A systematic review and meta-analysis of randomized controlled trials. *J Funct Foods.* 2015, DOI: 10.1016/j.jff.2015.01.005.

Simon GE, Von Korff M, Saunders K, Miglioretti DL, Crane PK, van Belle G, Kessler RC. Association between obesity and psychiatric disorders in the US adult population. *Arch Gen Psychiatry.* 2006;63(7):824-30.

Sharma RA, Euden SA, Platton SL, Cooke DN, Shafayat A, Hewitt HR, Marczylo TH, Morgan B, Hemingway D, Plummer SM, Pirmohamed M, Gescher AJ, Steward WP. Phase I clinical trial of oral curcumin: biomarkers of systemic activity and compliance. *Clin Cancer Res.* 2004;10: 6847-54.

Shoba G, Joy D, Joseph T, Majeed M, Rajendran R, Srinivas PS. Influence of piperine on the pharmacokinetics of curcumin in animals and human volunteers. *Planta Med.* 1998;64(4):353-56.

Vadhan-Raj S, Weber DM, Wang M, Giralt SA, Thomas SK, Alexanian R, ZhouX, Patel P, Bueso-Ramos CE, Newman RA, Aggarwal BB. Curcumin downregulates NF-κB and related genes in patients with Multiple myeloma: Results of a phase I/II study. *Blood* (ASH Annual Meeting Abstracts) 2007. Abstract 1177.

Volak LP, Hanley MJ, Masse G, Hazarika S, Harmatz JS, Badmaev V, Majeed M, Greenblatt DJ, Court MH. Effect of a herbal extract containing Curcumin and piperine on midazolam, flurbiprofen and paracetamol (acetaminophen) pharmacokinetics in healthy volunteers. *Br J Clin Pharm.* 2013;75(2): 450-62.

Woodbury-Farina M, Cernovsky Z, Chiu S, Bureau Y, Campbell R, Houicin J, Terpstra K, Raheb H, Husni M, Badmaev V. Proof of concept of randomized controlled study of Curcumin C3 Complex® as adjunct treatment in Schizophrenia: effects on negative and depressive symptoms. Cultivating Natural Bioactives: International Conference July 9—11, 2012 London,UK.

 

# Glossary

**5-FU**
5-fluorouracil - A drug commonly used in the treatment of cancer

**5-HETE**
5-Hydroxyeicosatetraenoic acid - A metabolite of arachidonic acid produced by numerous cells in mammals and implicated in aberrant pro-inflammatory immune responses

**ACF**
Aberrant Crypt Foci - Clusters of abnormal tube-like glands in the lining of the colon and rectum that aids in early detection of colorectal cancer

**Akt**
A serine/threonine-specific protein kinase that plays a key role in multiple cellular processes such as glucose metabolism, apoptosis, cell proliferation, transcription and cell migration

**AMPK**
5' adenosine monophosphate - activated protein kinase - An enzyme that plays a role in cellular energy homeostasis

**BAI**
Beck Anxiety Inventory - A 21-question multiple-choice self-report inventory that is used for measuring the severity of an individual's anxiety

**Bcl-2 and Bcl-xL**
Regulator proteins that induce to inhibit apoptosis or programmed cell death; Bcl-2 - B cell lymphoma 2

**BDI**
Beck Depression Inventory - A 21-question multiple-choice self-report inventory, used for measuring the severity of depression

**BDMC**
Bisdemethoxycurcumin - A natural demethoxy derivative of Curcumin

**CBR**
Clinical Benefit Response - An informal term which usually means anything other than progressive disease

**CDC**
Centre for Disease Control - One of the major operating components of the Department of Health and Human Services, USA

**cFLIP**
Cellular FADD-like IL-1$\beta$-converting enzyme-inhibitory protein - A programmed cell death regulator that can suppress TNF-$\alpha$

**CGRP**
Calcitonin Gene Related Peptides - A peptide produced in both peripheral and central neurons, it plays an important role in transmission of pain

**CHD**
Coronary Heart Disease - A condition in which plaques build up within the coronary arteries thus preventing the optimum supply of oxygen rich blood to heart muscles

**CHOP therapy**
Cyclophosphamide, Hydroxydaunorubicin, Oncovin and Prednisone therapy - A chemotherapy regimen used in the treatment of Non-Hodgkin's lymphoma

**c-Myc**
A regulator gene that codes for a protein that plays a key role in cell cycle progression, apoptosis and cellular transformation and its abnormal expression is associated with tumors

**COPD**
Chronic Obstructive Pulmonary Disease - A progressive disease that causes difficulty in breathing characterized by shortness of breath, cough, and sputum production

**COX-2**
Cycloxygenase-2 - An enzyme primarily responsible for inflammation and pain

**CYP2C9**
Cytochrome P450 2C9 - It is an enzyme that in humans is encoded by the CYP2C9 gene which plays a major role in oxidation

**CYP3A**
Cytochrome P450 3A - One of the most important cytochrome P450 isoforms responsible for drug metabolism by humans

**DLQI**
Dermatology Life Quality Index – A dermatology-specific Quality of Life instrument which consists of a simple 10-question validated questionnaire that can be used in over 40 different skin conditions

**DLT**
Dose Limiting Toxicity - Size-effects that are severe enough to prevent giving more of the treatment

**DMC**
Demethoxycurcumin - A natural demethoxy derivative of Curcumin

**EGCG**
Epigallocatechingallate - An ester of epigallo-catechin and gallic acid found abundantly in tea having potential use as a therapeutic for a broad range of disorders

**ELISA**
Enzyme linked Immunosorbant Assay - A common laboratory technique which is used to measure the concentration of an analyte (usually antibodies or antigens) in solution

**FAP**
Familial Adenomatous Polyposis - An inherited disorder characterized by cancer of the large intestine (colon) and rectum

**FEV1**
Forced Expiratory Volume in one second - It is the volume of air that can forcibly be blown out in one second

**FVC**
Forced Vital Capacity - The amount of air which can be forcibly exhaled from the lungs after taking the deepest breath possible

**GSH**
Reduced Glutathione - A reduced form of Glutathione, it is a potent antioxidant in plants, animals, bacteria and fungi.

**GST**
Glutathione-S-transferase - Belongs to a family of Phase II detoxification enzymes that have the primary role to detoxify xenobiotics by catalyzing the conjugation of the reduced form of glutathione (GSH)

**HADS**
Hospital Anxiety and Depression Scale - A measure used by doctors to determine the levels of anxiety and depression that a patient is experiencing

**HDL**
High Density Lipoprotein - Commonly known as "good cholesterol", increasing concentrations of HDL particles are strongly associated with decreasing accumulation of atherosclerosis within the walls of arteries and hence lower risk of cardiovascular diseases

**HPA axis**
Hypothalamic-pituitary-adrenal axis - A complex set of reactions, signals and feedback interactions between the hypothalamus, pituitary gland and adrenal cortex that have an influence on stress and other natural processes such as digestion, immune system, energy and mood.

**HRCT**
High Resolution Computed Tomography - A scanning protocol used in the diagnosis of various health problems

**hs-CRP**
High-sensitivity C-reactive Protein - A protein that increases in the blood with inflammation, it is used as a measure to assess the risk of heart diseases

**Hsp**
Heat Shock Protein - Family of proteins that are produced in response to stress such as heat, cold, UV radiations, wounds and so on

**IL**
Interleukin - Cytokines expressed by white blood cells that play a very important role in all aspects of inflammation and immunity

**iNOS**
Inducible nitric oxide synthase - Key enzyme generating Nitric oxide and plays an important in numerous physiological and pathophysiological (including inflammation, infection etc.) conditions

**JNK**
Jun amino terminal kinases - They are responsible to stress stimuli and play a role in T-cell differentiation and cellular apoptosis pathway

**KGF**
Keratinocyte Growth Factor - A growth factor present in the epithelialization-stage of wound healing

**LDL**
Low Density Lipoprotein - Also referred to as "bad cholesterol", it is one of the five major groups of lipoproteins which when oxidized and enter the endothelium, pose a threat for cardiovascular diseases

**LOX**
Lipoxygenase - Iron containing enzyme that catalyses the addition of molecular oxygen to polyunsaturated fatty acids to make them saturated fatty acid hyperoxides

**LPFI**
Lequesne's Pain Functional Index - An Index of severity for Osteo arthritis for the knee

**$M_1G$**
Pyrimido[1,2-a]purin-10(3H)-one - A heterocyclic compound due to lipid peroxidation caused by malondialdehyde that may further lead to mutagenesis and act as a potent carcinogen

**MCP 1**
Monocyte Chemotactic Protein 1 - An important chemokine (signalling protein) that regulates migration and infiltration of monocytes/ macrophages

**MDA**
Malondialdehyde - An important marker for lipid peroxidation / oxidative stress

**MDD**
Major Depressive Disorder - Mental disorder characterized by persistent low mood

**Met S**
Metabolic Syndrome - A group of conditions - increased blood pressure, a high blood sugar level, excess body fat around the waist and abnormal cholesterol levels - that occur together, tus increasing the risk of heart disease, stroke and diabetes

**MGUS**
Monoclonal Gammopathy of Undetermined Significance - A condition in which abnormal proteins are present in the blood that can progress for years with no symptoms finally leading to other lymphoproliferative disorders

**MMP**
Matrix Metalloproteinase - Calcium dependant endopeptidase responsible for tissue remodeling and degradation of the extracellular matrix

**MOMI**
Modified Oral Mucositis Index - A measurement of severity of Oral Mucositis

**NCEP**
ATPIII Criteria - Globally accepted criteria used for diagnosing Metabolic Syndrome

**NF-κB**
Nuclear Factor-κB - A protein complex involved in cellular response to stress

**NHL**
Non-Hodgkin's lymphoma - A cancer that originates in the lymphatic system where tumors develop from lymphocytes, a type of white blood cell

**NSAIDs**
Non-steroidal Anti-Inflammatory Drugs - A class of drugs that provides analgesic (pain-killing), antipyretic (fever-reducing) and anti-inflammatory effects

**OA**
Osteoarthritis - A degenerative chronic condition of the joints accompanied by pain, stiffness and swelling.

**OLP**
Oral Lichen Planus - An inflammatory condition affecting the mucous membranes in the mouth

**OM**
Oral mucositis - Mucositis or tissue swelling in the mouth caused due to chempotherapy or radiation therapy

**OMAS**
Oral Mucositis Assessment Scale - Commonly used measure for severity of oral mucositis

**p53, p21**
Tumor suppressor protein that protects from DNA damage

**PASI**
Psoriasis Area Severity Index - An index used to express the severity of psoriasis with respect to erythema, induration, desquamation and percentage of affected area

**PGA**
Physician's Global Assessment - A score given by a physician for the improvement of a condition taking into account several factors

**PGE2**
Prostaglandin E2 - An essential homeostatic factor that is released in response to infection or inflammation

**PRISMA**
Preferred Reporting Items for Systematic Reviews and Meta-Analysis - An evidence-based minimum set of items (check lists and flow diagrams) for reporting in systematic reviews and meta-analyses

**QOL**
Quality of Life - Measurement of general well being of individuals

**RBC**
Red Blood Cell - Common type of blood cells responsible for oxygen delivery to body tissues

**rFLC**
Free Light Chain Ratio - A testing method used to help detect, diagnose, and monitor plasma cell disorders in conditions such as multiple myeloma

**ROS**
Reactive Oxygen Species - Chemically reactive molecules containing oxygen that are formed as a natural by-product of the normal metabolism of oxygen and have an important role in cell signalling and homeostasis

**SCORAD**
Scoring Atopic Dermatitis - A clinical tool used to assess the extent and severity of eczema

**SCFE**
Super Critical Fluid Extraction - Use of supercritical fluids as extraction solvent

**SM**
Sulphur Mustard - Commonly known as Mustard Gas, it is cytotoxic and a chemical warfare agent that cause blisters on the exposed skin and in lungs

**SOD**
Superoxide Dismutase - An enzyme found in all living cells that catalyzes the destruction of the oxygen free radical and thus protects oxygen-metabolizing cells against harmful effects of superoxide free-radicals

**STAT3**
Signal Transducer and Activator of Transcription 3 - Protein encoded by this gene mediates the expression of a variety of genes in response to cell stimuli, and thus plays a key role in many cellular processes such as cell growth and apoptosis

**SULT**
Sulfotransferase - An enzyme that catalyzes the sulfate conjugation of several pharmacologically important endo- and xenobiotics

**TGF-β**
Transforming growth factor-β - A family of cytokines that play important roles in growth and development, inflammation and repair and host immunity

**TNF-α**
Tumor Necrosis Factor-alpha - A cytokine (small protein) that causes programmed cell death

**UGT**
Uridine 5'-diphospho-glucuronosyltransferase - An enzyme that catalyzez the glucuronidation reaction

**VAS**
Visual Analog Scale - A measurement instrument for subjective characteristics or attitudes that cannot be directly measured with the help of questionnaires

**VEGF**
Vascular Endothelial Growth Factor - A signal protein that promotes the growth of new blood vessels to restore blood supply to cells and tissues

**WBC**
White Blood Cell - Cells of the immune system responsible for protecting the body from infectious diseases

**WOMAC**
Western Ontario and McMaster Universities Osteoarthritis Index - A proprietary set of standardized questionnaires used by health professionals to evaluate the condition of patients with osteoarthritis developed at Western Ontario and McMaster Universities in 1982